C000297524

FLORA
OF THE
CANARY ISLANDS

POCKET GUIDE

David Bramwell

Editorial Rueda

Porto Cristo, 13 (Parque Lisboa)
28924 Alcorcón (Madrid)
Tel.: (91) 619 27 79 · Fax: (91) 610 28 55

KEY TO DISTRIBUTION:

LANZAROTE .... L.
FUERTEVENTURA .... F.
GRAN CANARIA .... C.
TENERIFE .... T.
GOMERA .... G.
LA PALMA .... P.
EL HIERRO .... H.

Photographs:
Zöe I. Bramwell
David Bramwell

I.S.B.N.: 84-7207-103-0
Depósito Legal M- 551-1998
Imprime: Tecnología Gráfica S.L
Ingles

To Alex, Vicky and Danny

Index

Introduction

The Canary Islands already have a number of books and catalogues which deal with the subject of the flora. Most of these, however, are scientific publications which are beyond the reach of the average tourist or layman merely interested in naming the plants that can be seen during a visit to the islands. Very few of these attempt to put common names to the plants or deal with their value as ornamental or medicinal subjects and this book is a first attempt to remedy this need.

Obviously in a Spanish-speaking group of islands most of the local plants do not have everyday English names so I have attempted to equate the Canarian plants with species of the British and Mediterranean floras which do have English common names. I have had to «invent» a number of these but I hope that by associating the local flora with familiar plants this will aid both identification and understanding of the Canarian flora.

This pocket guide which includes almost three hundred Canary plants and a brief introduction to the plant communities and vegetation of the islands, complements the more complete «Wild Flowers of the Canary Islands» which has keys and descriptions of all the plants included here. For a fairly comprehensive guide to the garden plants of the Canaries I recommend the book «Subtropical Gardens» which is also published by Editorial Rueda.

Many Canarian plants are threatened with extinction and the recognition that the local flora and vegetation together form an important tourist attraction will be an important factor in deciding their survival and I hope that this «popular» guide helps to contribute to that objective.

David Bramwell

Reichardia famarae
FAMARA HAWKBIT

VEGETATION OF THE CANARY ISLANDS

THE LOWER ZONE

The lower zone of the islands consists of a coastal belt below 100 m. and an extensive belt of xerophytic vegetation which gives way, at its upper limit, to the forest zone.

The rocky coast vegetation is often dominated by the sweet spurge (*Euphorbia balsamifera*) or the leafless spurge (*E. aphylla*). Several specifically coastal plants such as Canary samphire (*Astydamia latifolia*), sea-lavender (*Limonium pectinatum*) and bean-caper (*Zygophyllum fontanesii*) consistently accompany the spurges.

In some areas, such as Maspalomas on Gran Canaria and Corralejo and Jandia on Fuerteventura, extensive areas of sand-dunes have developed and these have a special flora in which species such as the tamarisk (*Tamarix canariensis*) are frequent. The dune vegetation has several non-endemic plants, some of which like *Traganum moquinii* (balancón) and *Salsola* and *Sueda* species are important sand stabilizers. The Fuerteventura dune communities have several interesting local endemics such as *Androcymbium psammophilum* (sand crocus), and local forms of the Mediterranean sea daffodil (*Pancratium maritimum*) and restharrow (*Ononis natrix*).

The coastal zone is replaced above 100 m. by the shrubby spurge communities which are so typical of the Canary Islands. They are dominated by the cactus-like *Euphorbia canariensis* and the succulent shrubs, *E. regis-jubae* on Lanzarote, Fuerteventura and Gran Canaria or *E. broussonetii* on Tenerife and the western islands. On La Gomera this species is replaced by *E. berthelotii* in the east and south-east of the island. The shrubby spurge communities are extremely species rich with a host of endemic plants amongst which the sow-thistles (*Sonchus spp.*), Paris daisies (*Argyranthemum spp.*) and houseleeks (*Aeonium spp.*) are prominent.

In the drier ravine beds, groves of the Canary date palm (*Phoenix canariensis*) can be found and in extremely dry conditions where the spurge vegetation does not develop it is substituted by the wire-like *Launaea arborescens* and the balo (*Plocama pendula*). On Fuerteventura several unique, xerophytic communities are to be found, the most interesting being the *Euphorbia handiensis* vegetation of the south of the Jandia peninsula and the colonies of *Caralluma burchardii*, a small, square-stemmed succulent which occurs amongst rocks and volcanic debris at various points of the island, on the islet of Lobos and also on Lanzarote.

i.   Palm groves and Tamarisks at Las Salinas, Fuerteventura. A palm grove in the bed of a dry ravine on the east coast of the island.

ii.   Dense vegetation of the Famara cliffs at El Bosque, Lanzarote. A community with the endemic *Ferula lancerottensis* and *Nauplius intermedius*.

iii

iv

iii.   One of the richest areas of lower zone vegetation at the Punta de Teno, Tenerife. This area is dominated by shrubby spurge and cardón but has a large number of local endemics in the community especially on the coastal cliffs.

iv.   Vegetation of a coastal lava flow at Güimar, Tenerife with cardón, sea rosemary and asparagus.

vi

v

vii

v.   Cliff vegetation of the northwest of Gran Canaria with Paris daisy and houseleeks. In many areas the coastal vegetation of the islands has been destroyed by tourist development and the remaining natural areas should be protected.

vi.   A threatened plant community on the coast of Gran Canaria at Arinaga. In this locality there is an important representation of local endemic species such as the Arinaga trefoil (*Lotus arinagensis*).

vii.   The extensive dune vegetation in the Corralejo Park at the north-east corner of Fuerteventura. This is the floristically most important dune complex in the Canary islands.

THE LAUREL FOREST ZONE

Laurel forests occur on all the Canary Islands except Lanzarote and Fuerteventura. They occupy a zone on the northern slopes of the islands between 600 and 1500 m. usually where the cloud layer, formed by the North East Trade Winds meeting the high mountains, considerably increases the precipitation and maintains humidity in the dry Summer months. It also develops in climatically favourable places on the southern slopes, for example at the Badajoz ravine at the head of the Güimar valley.

This type of forest is dominated by trees of the family Lauraceae but is also rich in other tree species, about 18 in all, and in forest-floor plants. Many of these, such as the cinerarias, ferns, violets, false sages and houseleeks are insular or local endemics. Others occur in similar vegetation throughout the Canary Islands (crane's bill, figwort etc.) and some even on Madeira (buttercup and St.John's wort).

In drier areas of the forest zone a formation known locally as fayal-brezal with wax-myrtle (*Myrica faya*) and tree-heath (*Erica arborea*) occurs. This is a more uniform woodland with a smaller variety of trees and forest-floor species.

The most important laurel forest areas in the Canaries are the Anaga mountains on Tenerife and, especially, the Garajonay National Park and World Heritage Site in the centre of the island of La Gomera. A small, but interesting, area of laurel forest is all that survives of this formation on Gran Canaria. This can be found at Los Tiles de Moya on the north side of the island. It is a small relict of a few hectares but is very rich in species with two almost exclusive endemics, the Moya foxglove (*Isoplexis chalcantha*) and the false sage (*Sideritis discolor*).

Other extremely good areas of laurel forest are to be found at El Canal on La Palma and in the Frontera region of El Hierro, an area with an important concentration of local and endemic species such as the shrubby burnet (*Bencomia sphaerocarpa*).

i

ii

i.   The laurel forest at Los Tiles de Moya on Gran Canaria. This small relict area has several interesting species such as *Bencomia caudata* and endemic foxgloves and false sage.

ii.   The tree-heath and wax-myrtle woodland which occupies drier or degraded areas in the laurel forest zone is a spectacular formation but is less rich in forest floor species.

iii

iv

iii.   The laurel forests of La Gomera have been declared both a national park and a UNESCO World Heritage Site. They are the least disturbed laurel forests in the Atlantic Islands.

iv.   The Anaga mountains have a large laurel forest along the crests and in the ravines on both northern and southern slopes. the area has one of the most complete forest floras in the archipelago.

v

vi

v.   The Anaga mountains laurel forests have been seriously threatened in the past by over-exploitation and the introduction of many weed species which compete for space with the local flora. The area has now been declared a Rural Park in the hope that further deterioration can be prevented and some of the area's original splendour restored.

vi.   The wild cinerarias are amongst the most beautiful species of the laurel forests. Each species is usually restricted to a single island. *Pericallis steetzii* is extremely common in the forest regions of the island of La Gomera. it is very varible in flower colour.

THE PINE FOREST ZONE

Natural Canarian pine forest is, like most pine forests, a superficially monotonous forest dominated by a single species, *Pinus canariensis*. The uniformity of the forest is, however, compensated by the spectacular scenery and landscape usually associated with it.

In the Canaries pine forest is found on Gran Canaria, Tenerife, El Hierro and La Palma. It is generally an open, savanna-like formation with few herbs and shrubs in the ground layer and extensive areas covered only by pine needles. The most common shrubs in the pine ecosystem are the sticky broom (*Adenocarpus foliolosus*) and the Canary gum (*Cistus symphytifolius*). Savories (*Micromeria* spp.) and trefoils (*Lotus* spp.) are also abundant in almost all the pine forests of the archipelago.

Several local endemics are sometimes found in the pine forests. This include some of the rarest species in the Canaries such as the rock-rose (*Helianthemum bystropogophyllum*) and savory (*Micromeria pineolens*) from Gran Canaria, the Hierro broom (*Adenocarpus ombriosus*) and a strange intermediate between sow-thistle and lettuce (*Lactucosonchus webbii*) from the north of La Palma.

On Gran Canaria and Tenerife the pine forests have been extensively replanted over the last forty years and these «new» forests are, in many areas now important semi-natural areas of mature forest. They now play an important role in the protection of watersheds and prevention of soil erosion as well as havens for such valuable pine forest fauna as the endemic blue chaffinch and the Canary woodpecker.

i

ii

i.   The pine forest cliffs of the Caldera de Taburiente, La Palma, house one of the richest floras of endemic species in the archipelago. These include local bugloss, burnet and hawkbit species.

ii.   In the south of Gran Canaria the pine forests merge with palms and spurges in a transition zone which is extemely rich in local endemics. In the past the pine forests probably extended into the dry valleys of this region.

iii

iv

iii.　　On the island of Tenerife the pine forests reach almost to 1900 m. and are often subjected to the most extreme winter climate in the archipelago.

iv.　　On Gran Canaria the high mountain region have been extensively repopulated with Canary pine which is now beginning to produce mature forests which can contribute to the re-establishment of the natural ecosystems.

v

vi

v.   The contrast between the old umbrella-shaped, mature pines and the recently planted, erect young trees is observable at the Mirador de Las Pinos de Galdar on Gran Canaria.

vi.   The Taburiente National Park on La Palma was established to protect one of the most important areas of pine forest in the Canary Islands.

THE HIGH MOUNTAIN ZONE

The vegetation of the highest mountain regions of Gran Canaria, Tenerife and La Palma consists of a shrub community virtually without trees and dominated by the Leguminosae family. The richest communities are, undoubtedly those of the Teide National Park on Tenerife with their remarkable concentration of endemic species. In the Teide Park the white broom (*Spartocytisus supranubius*) and the sticky broom (*Adenocarpus viscosus*) are dominant but there are numerous other endemics such as the Teide daisy, the shrubby scabious (*Pterocephalus lasiospermus*), the flixweeds (*Descurainia bourgaeana* and *D. gonzalezii*) and many others which are important components of the ecosystem.

Probably the best known plants from the National Park are the bugloss species, *Echium wildpretii* and *E. auberianum*, and the Teide violet, *Viola cheiranthifolia*. The Park, however, is still capable of providing surprises and a new rockrose, *Helianthemum juliae*, was only discovered a few years ago.

The mountain zone of La Palma is restricted in area to the rim of the Tabouriente caldera but, nevertheless, it is an area rich in local endemics and shares many species with the Teide. Specific local endemics include the broom, *Genista benehoavensis*, the bugloss, *Echium gentianoides*, and the violet, *Viola palmensis*. Species also found in Las Cañadas del Teide include the Teide burnet, *Bencomia exstipulata*, the Teide knapweed, *Cheirolophus teydis* and the red bugloss, *Echium wildpretii*.

On Gran Canaria the mountain zone is rather different and very few species are shared with other islands. The dominant shrubs are the yellow, small-leaved broom (*Teline microphylla*) and the mountain scabious (*Pterocephalus dumetorum*). The rich community has several species of savory, false sage, houseleek, flixweed and sow-thistle and though less exalted than the Teide Park community is certainly no less rich or interesting.

i.   The La Palma violet from the highest peaks of the upper rim of the Caldera de Tabouriente. This is a close relative of the rather better known Teide violet.

ii.   *Descurainia bourgeauana*, one of a number of flixweeds found in all the high mountain region of the Canary islands. This species is a local endemic of the Las Cañadas region of Tenerife.

iii.   In the dry summer months the Teide flixweed justifies its local name of hierba pajonera or straw-shrub.

iv.   The high mountain zone of Gran Canaria is rich in local endemics with relatively few connections with similar zones on Tenerife and La Palma. The cliffs of the Roque Nublo complex have a number of endangered local species and contribute to the need for special protection for this area which has been proposed as a National Park.

iv

v

v. Undoubtedly the species which survive in the highest mountains of the Canary Islands are subjected to extreme fluctuations of temperature. In the winter months they may spend lengthy periods beneath snow and ice and in the summer have to survive long, dry spells with temperatures between 35 and 40 degrees Celsius.

vi. Yellow broom, false sage and wild savory in the high mountains of Gran Canaria in the proposed Nublo National Park. These, with many other endemics of Gran Canaria, form part of the unique vegetation of the area.

vi

1 CANARY ISLANDS PINE $\qquad$ PINACEAE

Pinus canariensis Chr.Sm. ex DC

A widely distributed species occurring on the western and central islands where it forms extensive forests except on La Gomera where it is rare. It usually inhabits the drier mountain areas between 1000 and 2000 m.asl. The Canary pine is very fire resistant and the heartwood (tea) was, in the past widely used for the construction of balconies, doors, beams etc. It was also used for the extraction of resin and turpentine. The species is often used as an ornamental tree and in reafforestation. It is propagated from seed and grows rapidly. (C.T.G.P.H.)

2 CANARY CEDAR $\qquad$ CUPRESSACEAE

Juniperus cedrus Webb & Berth.

A rare endemic species of the Canary Islands and Madeira and is, at the present time, restricted to the highest mountains of Tenerife and La Palma and the Montaña del Cedro on the west side of Gran Canaria. It occurs between 500 and 2000 m. and was, in the past, probably much more widely distributed. The aromatic wood was traditionally used for making chests and boxes and on Madeira for lining the roof of churches. The Canary cedar is an attractive ornamental species and is propagated from seed. (C.T.P.G.)

3 CANARY JUNIPER $\qquad$ CUPRESSACEAE

Juniperus canariensis Guyot

The Canary juniper is an endemic species closely related to junipers of the Mediterranean region. It is currently found on the central and western islands of the archipelago and in some places, for example the northern slopes of La Gomera, it is very common forming an open woodland known as sabinal. On the other islands it is rather more rare because of its exploitation as fuel-wood and for charcoal production. It makes a useful ornamental shrub in drier climates and is propagated from seed which germinates rather slowly. (C.T.G.P.H.)

$$\frac{1}{2 \mid 3}$$

4 CANARY ISLANDS WAX-MYRTLE   MYRICACEAE
Myrica faya Aiton

This small tree is found on the central and western Canary Islands, Madeira and the Azores as well as in small enclaves on the west coast of Portugal. It is common in the humid forests of the islands especially in association with the tree heath, Erica arborea in a community known as fayal-brezal which occurs in the laurel forest zone between 500 and 1500 m. The small, waxy, black berries formed part of the diet of the original inhabitants (guanches) of the islands and the wood has been traditionally used for making charcoal. The wax-myrtle is probably extinct on the islands of Lanzarote and Fuerteventura.
(C.T.G.P.H.)

5 CANARY WILLOW   SALICACEAE
Salix canariensis Chr.Sm.

A tall shrub or small tree up to 10 m. which is usually associated with running water in the beds of ravines and in the laurel and pine forest on all the islands except Lanzarote and Fuerteventura. In some ravines such as the Barranco del Infierno on Tenerife and Barranco de los Cernicalos on Gran Canaria the Canary willow forms dense thickets known as saucedas. The bark, leaves and flowers of this willow have analgesic and antispasmodic properties and are used in local folk medicine. (C.T.G.P.H.)

6 TREE PELLITORY   URTICACEAE
Gesnouinia arborea (L.) Gaud.

This is a tall shrub which occurs in the laurel forest zones of the central and western Canaries. The Genus *Gesnouinia* is, in fact, endemic to the Islands and contains only this species. Its usual habitat is in shady, humid places generally close to springs or running water. The tree pellitory is rather rare but can be locally abundant in particular places such as the Chorros de Epina on La Gomera. Its pinkish inflorescence of small, star-like flowers make it an attractive plant for shady corners in a garden. It is easily propagated from seed. (C.T.G.P.H.)

$$\frac{4}{5} \mid 6$$

7 NARROW-LEAVED FORSKOLEA   URTICACEAE
Forsskahlea angustifolia Retz.

This species occurs in the Canary and Cape Verde Islands. It is a common, almost weedy small shrub or herbaceous perennial in the lower zone amongst the *Euphorbia* vegetation and along the roadsides and abandoned fields. It is considered locally to be a valuable medicinal plant and is used for treating fevers and rashes as well as an anti-inflamatory. In the Canaries it is found on all the islands and most of the small islets. (L.F.C.T.G.P.H.)

8 CANARY ISLANDS SORREL   POLYGONACEAE
Rumex lunaria L.

An extremely common species found on all the Islands, this plant is a colonizer of open habitats such as roadsides and cinder cones particularly in the lower and laurel forest zones. It grows very rapidly and has the advantage that it can be planted and clipped into a hedge. Locally it is frequently used as a medicinal plant especially as an anti-inflamatory and as a decongestant. It is endemic to the Canary Islands but is now naturalized on some of the Mediterranean islands such as Sicily. (L.F.C.T.G.P.H.)

9 ATLANTIC ISLANDS BUTTERCUP   RANUNCULACEAE
Ranunculus cortusifolius Willd.

The Atlantic Islands buttercup occurs in the Canary Islands, Madeira and the Azores. It is locally very abundant in humid forest zones both in the laurel woodlands and the pines. It can also be found in the more humid, higher regions of the drier islands of Lanzarote and Fuerteventura where it has a rather dwarfed habit. It is a useful ornamental plant for shady gardens and can be grown from seed. Locally it is used medicinally to treat haemorrhoids and as an analgesic. (L.F.C.T.G.P.H.)

7

8

9

10 CANARIAN WALL PELLITORY   U R T I C A C E A E

Parietaria filamentosa Webb & Berth.

A small woody-based plant, this pellitory is found only on the islands of Tenerife and La Palma where it is locally common. Its natural habitat is on shady cliffs in the lower zone between 200 and 500 m.though it is well adapted to living on stone walls. It has no value as an ornamental plant but is sometimes used medicinally as a diuretic and for treating renal disorders. (T.P.)

11 CANARY ISLANDS NETTLE   U R T I C A C E A E

Urtica morifolia Poir.

This large, woody-based nettle occurs in the laurel forests of the Canaries on the islands of Gran Canaria,Tenerife, La Palma, La Gomera and El Hierro where it is locally frequent in woodlands between 500 and 1400 m. It is a stinging nettle which can produce a severe rash but, nevertheless, it is used locally as a medicinal plant to treat tuberculosis and as a hair tonic. (C.T.G.P.H.)

10

11

THE LAURELS   LAURACEAE

In the Canary Islands there are four species of trees belonging to the laurel family. These are *Laurus azorica, Apollonias barbujana, Persea indica* and *Ocotea foetens*. These form the dominant elements of the Atlantic Islands laurel forest known as laurisilva which reaches its maximum development in the Canarian archipelago.

12 CANARIAN LAUREL   *Laurus azorica* (Seub.) Franco

The Canarian laurel is a tree which can grow to 20 metres. It has aromatic glandular leaves and cream-coloured flowers. The fruits are oval berries with a single seed. The laurel is the most common of the forest trees and occurs on the central and western Canaries as well as on Madeira and the Azores. (C.T.G.P.H.)

12

13 CANARIAN MAHOGANY *Apollonias barbujana* (Cav.) Bornm.

A species found in the Canaries and Madeira, the Canarian mahogany or barbusano usually occurs in the drier parts of the laurel forest and at the transition between this and the lower zone. It has distinctive glossy and somewhat curled leaves and differs from the laurel by having hermaphrodite flowers. The wood was traditionally used in the Canaries for making high quality furniture. (C.T.G.P.H.)

14 CANARY ISLANDS EBONY   *Persea indica* (L.) Spreng.

Despite its name this species is a native of Madeira and the Canary Islands. The confusion probably arose because the first plants were brought to England on board tea clippers which traded with India but passed through Madeira and the Canaries during their voyage. It is a handsome species which forms a large, spreading tree with bluish-green leaves. (C.T.G.P.H)

13

14

15 MADEIRA LAUREL or GREENHEART

Ocotea foetens (Ait.) Benth.

This species is easily distinguished from the other laurels by the two glands at the base of the leaf and by its acorn-like fruits. It occupies the shadiest, more humid niches in the laurel forest and is the rarest of the group. The wood is strong smelling but has a hard, ebony-like texture. (C.T.G.P.H.)

15

16 FOUNTAIN BUSH   AMARANTHACEAE
Bosea yervamora L.

A small endemic bush with arched branches and reddish fruits which may turn black when fully mature. Its nearest relatives are found on the island of Cyprus and in SW Asia.It is locally common on the northern slopes of the lower zone of the central and western islands between 200 and 600 m. The fruits are much appreciated by local birds such as the Canary black-cap and blackbird. The leaves are said to induce abortion in livestock. It can be used as a hedge plant and tolerates annual pruning. (C.T.G.P.H.)

17 LANZAROTE CHICKWEED   CARYOPHYLLACEAE
Minuartia platyphylla (Christ) McNeill

A rather rare local endemic of the cliffs of Famara on Lanzarote and Jandia on Fuerteventura this species is rather variable in habit, leaf-size and in flower colour which ranges from white to deep pink. In its natural habitat it suffers from overgrazing and is generally confined to rather inaccessible places. It can be used as a rock-garden plant in frost-free areas and can be propagated from seed. (L.F.)

18 GOMERAN ALL-SEED   CARYOPHYLLACEAE
Dicheranthus plocamoides Webb

The Gomeran all-seed is a dwarf shrublet which is found on the island of La Gomera particularly on the cliffs and in rocky areas of the north and west between 100 and 500 m. It also occurs on the ancient rocks of the western end of Tenerife between Los Silos in the north and Tamaimo. The genus *Dicheranthus* with only this single species, is endemic to the Canary Islands. It has no known medicinal uses but is potentially of interest as a rock-garden subject. (T.G.)

16

17

18

19 GOMERAN CAMPION — CARYOPHYLLACEAE
Silene bourgaei Webb ex Christ

This rather attractive white-flowered campion is confined to the island of La Gomera where it is rather rare. It is found only on cliffs in the north and west between Agulo and Vallehermoso at 300-500 m. There are a number of related species on the other islands, notably *S. sabinosae* on El Hierro, *S. pogonocalyx* on La Palma, *S. lagunensis* on Tenerife and *S.tamaranae* on Gran Canaria. They are all of minor ornamental value and can be propagated from seed. (G.)

20 SUCCULENT ALL-SEED — CARYOPHYLLACEAE
Polycarpaea carnosa Chr.Sm.

The succulent all-seed is a cliff plant which occurs on the two extreme ends of Tenerife and on the west side of La Gomera. It is generally associated with ancient rock-formations and is found in shady crevices and on rock-ledges where its fleshy leaves help it to resist drought. On the island of La Gomera it is said that infusions of this plant have a diuretic effect. Several other species of *Polycarpaea* are found in the Canaries including *P. nivea* from Tenerife, Gran Canaria, Lanzarote and Fuerteventura, *P. smithii* from La Palma and *P. teneriffae* from all the islands. (G.T.)

21 CANARY ISLANDS KNOT-GRASS — CARYOPHYLLACEAE
Paronychia canariensis Juss.

A locally abundant woody shrublet from the central and western Canary Islands, the Canary knot-grass grows in the lower, xerophytic zone on cliffs and amongst rocks in the *Euphorbia* communities. It has local medicinal uses, an infusion being used for the treatment of chest infections. As an ornamental plant it has considerable potential value as ground-cover and it is easily propagated from cuttings or seed. (C.T.G.P.H.)

21

19 | 20

22 TREE SEA-KALE CRUCIFERAE
Crambe arborea Webb ex Christ

A tall shrub up to 2m, this is the largest of the Canary Islands sea-kales. It is endemic to the island of Tenerife where it is found on the cliffs of the Ladera de Guimar in the south. The leaves are variable, from deeply divided to almost entire and are sometimes used for flavouring soups. The mass of white flowers make it an attractive garden subject. This species is one of about a dozen which are found only in the Canary Islands and Madeira. (T.)

23 GRAN CANARIAN SEA-KALE CRUCIFERAE
Crambe pritzelii Bolle

This rather rough-leaved species is confined to forests and shady cliffs on the island of Gran Canaria where it is locally frequent between 400 and 800 m. It has near relatives in *C. strigosa* of the western Canaries and Tenerife and *C. gomeraea* which is endemic to La Gomera. It is potentially useful as a garden plant because of its large inflorescence but the leaves are subject to attack by butterfly larvae. It is propagated from seed. (C.)

24 CANARY ISLANDS ALISON CRUCIFERAE
Lobularia canariensis (DC) Borgen

The Canary alyssum is widely distributed throughout the Atlantic Islands and is abundant on all the Canary Islands. It occurs in the lower and forest zones to over 1000 m. especially in dry rocky places. It is very similar to the gardener's sweet alyssum and has considerable potential as an annual bedding plant for drier climates. A more robust form sometimes known as *Lobularia palmensis* is found on the island of La Palma. (L.F.C.T.G.P.H.)

22 | 23

24

25 CANARY FLIXWEED   CRUCIFERAE

Descurainia millefolia (Jacq.) Webb & Berth.

A widespread Canary Islands plant which occurs on all the western islands and is particularly common along the north coast of Tenerife between 200 and 1000 m. This and several related species are sometimes used in local folk medicine as an expectorant. The species is generally not found in cultivation though its finely divided leaves and yellow flowers suggest that it could have some potential as a garden plant. (T.G.P.H.)

26 MOUNTAIN FLIXWEED   CRUCIFERAE

Descurainia preauxiana Webb ex O.E. Schulz

The mountain flixweed is confined to the south-central mountain region of the island of Gran Canaria where it is locally frequent on the cliffs of the deep ravines between 400 and 1600 m. It is easily distinguishable from the other species of the genus because of its filiform leaf-lobes and its dense, terminal leaf-rosettes. It is not cultivated as a garden plant and no medicinal uses have been reported. (C.)

27 AGAETE FLIXWEED

Descurainia artemisoides Svent.

A rather rare species which is confined to the shady cliffs and rocks of the area between Agaete and Tirma on the island of Gran Canaria, the Agaete flixweed is very similar in habit and leaf morphology to D. millefolia which does not occur on Gran Canaria. It has considerable potential as an ornamental plant but has no known medicinal properties. (C.)

25

26

27

28 CANARIAN SHRUBBY STOCK CRUCIFERAE
Parolinia ornata Webb

The shrubby stock is endemic to Gran Canaria where it is locally common in the Euphorbia communities of the southern slopes. The horned fruits which characterize the genus are unique in the Cruciferae family of plants and *Parolinia* has its nearest relatives in the highlands of East Africa, S. Arabia and the island of Socotra. This species is sometimes used as an ornamental for its grey foliage and small pink flowers. It does not have any known medicinal uses. (C.)

29 CANARY MUSTARD CRUCIFERAE
Erucastrum cardaminoides (Webb) O.E.Schulz

A small, yellow-flowered herb with deeply lobed leaves, this mustard is found in dry habitats, fields, roadsides etc. in the lower zone of the islands. It is particularly frequent in some parts of the west of Gran Canaria between Agaete and the Aldea de San Nicolas. No medicinal properties have been reported though many of its near relatives are rich in vitamin C and are sometimes used in salads. (L? F.C.T.G.P.H.)

30 CANARY ISLANDS WALL-FLOWER CRUCIFERAE
Erysimum scoparium (Brouss.) Wetts.

This is a very common species found in the higher mountain regions of Tenerife, Gran Canaria and La Palma where it extends from the pine forests into the «subalpine» zone. It is one of the botanical features of Las Cañadas del Teide on Tenerife and of the Nublo Park on Gran Canaria. The Canary Wallflower has considerable ornamental value and is grown as a garden plant not only in the Canaries but also in other parts of the world. It is usually propagated from seed which is produced abundantly. (C.T.P.)

31 CANARY MIGNONETTE RESEDACEAE
Reseda crystallina Webb & Berth.

This plant, sometimes known as *Reseda lancerotae*, occurs on the islands of Lanzarote and Fuerteventura where it is quite common, and on Gran Canaria where it is confined to a small area of the west coast. Like several other *Reseda* species it has anti-inflamatory properties and is sometimes used in local folk medicine (Fuerteventura). A second endemic species *R. scoparia* is found in the coastal regions of the central and western islands. (L.F.C.)

	28
29	
30	31

The array of members of the spurge genus, *Euphorbia*, is one of the major features of the Canarian flora. The types of spurge found in the islands ranges from the cactus-like *E. canariensis* and *E. handiensis*, the leafless succulent *E. aphylla*, succulent-stemmed shrubs such as *E. broussonetii* and *E. atropurpurea* to small forest trees like *E. mellifera*. These plants form a direct link between the Canary islands and the ancient Tertiary Period floras of Africa and, as such, are of great historic and scientific interest.

32 JANDIA CACTUS-SPURGE

Euphorbia handiensis Burchd.

This fascinating species is found only in a few isolated localities towards the southern point of the Jandia peninsula on the island of Fuerteventura. It is considered to be in danger of extinction and is now strictly protected. Its nearest relatives are found on the Moroccan coast. (F.)

33 CANARY ISLANDS CACTUS-SPURGE

Euphorbia canariensis L.

A very common species on the western and central Canary Islands where it is often a dominant member of the vegetation of the lower zone (cardonales), *E. canariensis* is rather rarer on Lanzarote where it is found only in the Malpais de la Corona, and Fuerteventura where it occurs in a few localities in the south of the island. The somewhat poisonous latex is used locally as a purgative and was, in the past, also used as a fish poison. (L.F.C.T.G.P.H.)

34 LEAFLESS SPURGE

Euphorbia aphylla Brouss. ex Willd.

This is a locally common species which inhabits three of the Canary Islands, Gran Canaria, Tenerife and La Gomera. It is found on the north coasts in dry rocky or sandy habitats between sea-level and 150 m. The latex of *E. aphylla* is sometimes used to treat skin diseases. All three species of succulent are used locally as garden and park plants, especially *E. canariensis*. (C.T.G.)

35 PURPLE-FLOWERED SPURGE   EUPHORBIACEAE
Euphorbia atropurpurea Brouss.

This very attractive shrub with dark red flowers and bluish-green leaves is confined to the south and west of the island of Tenerife between Teno and Guimar. It is locally very common and is usually found in the dry zone communities with other *Euphorbia* species between 300 and 1200 m. At Teno a yellowish to green-flowered form is frequent, and both this and the typical form make good garden subjects. (T.)

36 COMMON CANARY SPURGE   EUPHORBIACEAE
Euphorbia regis-jubae Webb & Berth.

One of the most common of all the Canarian endemic plants, this species is dominant over large areas of the lower zone of the islands of Gran Canaria, Lanzarote and Fuerteventura. Its western counterpart, *E. broussonetii* Link, occupies a similar position on Tenerife, La Gomera, La Palma and El Hierro. The common Canary spurge is known locally as tabaiba and its latex, though poisonous, is said to have analgesic properties when applied externally to the skin. (L.F.C.)

37 GOMERA SPURGE   EUPHORBIACEAE
Euphorbia lambii Svent.

An endangered species which is found only on La Gomera where it occurs at the lower margins of the laurel forest. Most of its few populations are protected within the limits of the Garajonay National Park which is also a UNESCO World Heritage Site. It has a similar yellowish-green flowered relative, *E. bourgaeana* Gay, in the Guimar region of south Tenerife. No medicinal properties are known and the species is only cultivated by specialist collectors of succulent plants. (G.)

$$35 \begin{array}{|l} 36 \\ \hline 37 \end{array}$$

HOUSELEEKS   CRASSULACEAE

The largest group of endemic plants in the Canary Islands is the houseleek family (Crassulaceae) with four genera, *Aeonium, Monanthes, Greenovia* and *Aichryson. Aeonium* is the biggest genus with over 30 species and the family as a whole has over 60 species in the Canaries. They are found in all the vegetation zones from the coast to the highest mountains and on all the islands.

38 AUTUMN HOUSELEEK

Aeonium manriqueorum Bolle

A common species throughout the lower and forest zones of Gran Canaria where it is very characteristic of the lowland vegetation of the northern part of the island. It flowers in late Autumn whilst most of the other species of *Aeonium* are Spring-flowering. The Autumn houseleek has some medicinal uses and extracts of the juice are said to have tranquilizing properties. Several similar species occur on other islands, *A. holochrysum* on Tenerife and the western islands and *A. balsamiferum* on Lanzarote and Fuerteventura. (C.)

39

40

39 MOYA HOUSELEEK CRASSULACEAE
Aeonium virgineum Webb in Christ

A local endemic of the north and west of Gran Canaria, this species occurs in the laurel forest zone and on shady, north-facing cliffs in the lower zone. It has closely related species in similar ecological conditions on the islands of Tenerife (*A. canariense*), La Palma and El Hierro (*A. palmense*) and on La Gomera (*A. subplanum*). Several members of the group have medicinal properties such as diuretics, disinfectants and are also used to reduce fevers. They are often cultivated by specialist succulent collectors and can be propagated by offsets or from seed. (C.)

40 RED-LINED HOUSELEEK CRASSULACEAE
Aeonium rubrolineatum Svent.

This species is found only on the island of La Gomera where it occurs at the upper limits of the dry zone and the transition zone to the laurel forests between 600 and 1200 m. Its creamy-pink flowers and summer flowering period distinguish it from the other members of its group (*A. manriqueorum* etc.). It is often found in specialist succulent collections and has potential as a local garden subject. It can be propagated from seed or cuttings. (G.)

41 NOBLE HOUSELEEK

CRASSULACEAE

Aeonium nobile Praeger

The noble houseleek is the only red-flowered species of the genus *Aeonium*. It is confined to the island of La Palma where it is locally frequent in several localities in the south and west. It is one of the most attractive species and is an excellent garden subject prized by succulent plant collectors. *Aeonium nobile* was discovered in the early part of this Century by one of the most important botanical explorers of the Canary Islands, Dr. Oscar Burchard. (P.)

42 SAUCER HOUSELEEK

CRASSULACEAE

Aeonium tabulaeforme (Haw.) Webb & Berth.

One of the most spectacular houseleeks with its plate-like rosettes and long inflorescence of pale yellow flowers, this species is found only along the north coast of Tenerife where it is locally frequent. It is one of the features of the cliffs of the Rambla de Castro between San Juan de La Rambla and Puerto de la Cruz. It is a good subject for gardens, especially for rocks and walls and is easily propagated from seed. Several medicinal properties are attributed to the saucer houseleek including pain relief, healing skin wounds and the reduction of inflamation. (T.)

42

41

43 PINK HOUSELEEK CRASSULACEAE

Aeonium goochiae Webb & Berth.

An endemic species of the island of La Palma, the pink houseleek is one of the most beautiful of all the Canary Island succulents. It occurs mainly in the north-east of La Palma on shady cliffs in the forest and lower zones where it is locally common. Its pink, star-like flowers make it a good plant for rockeries and it is easily propagated from cuttings or seed. The juice has local medicinal uses especially in the reduction of inflamation. (P.)

44 VALVERDE HOUSELEEK CRASSULACEAE

Aeonium valverdense Praeger

This pale, pink-flowered species is confined to the small island of El Hierro where it is locally common amongst the dry rocks and lavas of the coastal region. It is one of the primary colonizers of recent lava flows on the island and survives very dry conditions. Its red-edged leaves and compact habit make it a potentially useful garden plant which is easily propagated from seed. (H.)

44 | 46
45 |

45 VALLEHERMOSO HOUSELEEK

CRASSULACEAE

Aeonium castello-paivae Bolle

A white to cream-flowered plant which is locally abundant in the lower zone of the island of La Gomera, this species is particularly common in the area between Hermigua and Vallehermoso. It is distinguished from the closely related A. decorum which also grows in the same region by its pale, not red-flushed leaves and pale flowers. It is propagated from cuttings or by seed and is often found in collections of succulent plants. (G.)

46 GIANT HOUSELEEK   CRASSULACEAE

Aeonium urbicum (Chr.Sm.) Webb & Berth.

One of the largest species, the giant houseleek occurs on two islands. It is common in the north and west of Tenerife and rare on La Gomera. On Tenerife the flower colour is variable from deep pink to pure white and in some areas the general variablity is increased due to hydridization with *A. ciliatum*. This species is a good garden subject and is propagated from seed. On Tenerife it is used in local folk medicine as a pain reliever and antinflamatory. (T.G.)

47

47 CAESPITOSE HOUSELEEK CRASSULACEAE

Aeonium simsii (Sweet) Stearn

A dwarf species forming clumps on rocks and in crevices in the central and southern mountains of Gran Canaria. It is locally very common and in its Spring flowering period can be quite spectacular with its golden-yellow inflorescences. In cultivation it is often found in collections of succulent plants as, unlike some of the larger *Aeonium* species, it can be grown in a small pot. It is propagated from offsets or from seed. In some areas of Gran Canaria this species forms extensive hybrid swarms with *Aeonium undulatum*. (C.)

48 STONE-CROP HOUSELEEK CRASSULACEAE

Aeonium sedifolium (Webb) Pit. & Proust

This very distinctive species has almost globular, succulent leaves which do not resemble those of any other Canarian houseleek. Its flowers, however, are similar to those of the other species on this page. The stone-crop houseleek is found on cliffs and in crevices of old basalt and phonolytic rocks on the western slopes of Tenerife from Los Silos to Guia de Isora, on La Palma in the extreme north west (El Time) and a small population also exists on La Gomera (Barranco Seco). It is often cultivated in succulent collections and no medicinal properties have been reported. It can be propagated by cuttings or from seed.

49 TEIDE HOUSELEEK CRASSULACEAE

Aeonium smithii (Sims) Webb & Berth.

A species which is easily distinguished from all the other houseleeks by its hairy stems and undulating leaf margins, the Teide houseleek is found only on the island of Tenerife. It is a small shrub of rocks and cliffs of the upper slopes of the south of the island and it extends into the highest regions in Las Cañadas del Teide (2200 m.). It is occasionally found in succulent plant collections but is rather difficult to keep. It is usually propagated from seed though it can be grown from cuttings. (T.)

47 | 48
49

50 ANNUAL HOUSELEEK　　　　　CRASSULACEAE
Aichryson laxum (Haw.) Bramwell

One of several annual houseleeks occurring in the Canary Islands, this species is found in the forest zones and in shady places in the lower zone of the western and central islands. It is one of a group of species with glandular-hairy stems and leaves (*A. porphyrogennetos* from Gran Canaria, *A. palmense* from La Palma etc.). A second group of glabrous species also occurs, the most common species of which are *A. punctatum* with a similar distribution and *A. pachycaulon* which is found on all the islands except Lanzarote and El Hierro. No medicinal properties have been attributed to the annual houseleeks. (C.T.G.P.H.)

51 GOLDEN HOUSELEEK　　　　　CRASSULACEAE
Greenovia aurea (Chr.Sm.) Webb & Berth.

The golden houseleek is distinguishable fron the other houseleek species by its dense rosette of blue-green leaves and its flowers with 30 to 35 petals. It lives on rocks, cliffs and walls, usually in shade, from the lower zone to the highest mountains and is locally very common. It is found on Gran Canaria, Tenerife and El Hierro but is replaced by *Greenovia diplocycla* on La Palma. Both species are found on La Gomera but *G. aurea* is rare. This species is often found in succulent collections and is an interesting garden plant for rockeries and stone walls. (C.T.G.H.)

52 FAMARA STONECROP　　　　　CRASSULACEAE
Sedum lancerottense Murray

From the Famara cliffs and Haria area of the north of Lanzarote, this small, yellow-flowered stonecrop is locally common. It is closely related to *Sedum nudum* from the island of Madeira and has no other relatives in the Canary Islands. It is rarely found in cultivation and no medicinal uses have been reported. It lives on some of the geologically oldest rocks on the island with many other local endemic species. (L.)

50

51

52

53 MINIATURE HOUSELEEK   CRASSULACEAE
Monanthes adenoscepes Svent.

One of 15 miniature houseleeks found in the Canary Islands and members of the genus Monanthes, this species is confined to the cliffs of the Guimar valley in the south of Tenerife. Its tiny flowers with large scale-like nectaries are typical of these houseleeks which are particularly common on the older rocks and forest cliffs of the central and western islands. They are frequently found in succulent collections but are not used as ornamentals or medicinally. (T.)

54 HIERRO SHRUBBY BURNET   ROSACEAE
Bencomia sphaerocarpa Svent.

A local endemic of the island of El Hierro, this species is extremely rare and can be considered to be in danger of extinction. It is confined to laurel forest cliffs above the village of Frontera where it occurs with several other local endemics. It has a more common relative *B. caudata*, which is found in the forests of Gran Canaria, Tenerife and La Palma and two very rare high mountain species *B. brachystachya* from Gran Canaria and *B. exstipulata* from Tenerife and La Palma. The sap is said to help heal superficial wounds and grazes. (H.)

55 RED SHRUBBY BURNET   ROSACEAE
Marcetella moquiniana (Webb & Berth.) Svent.

Found on the islands of Gran Canaria, Tenerife and La Gomera, this rather rare species is most likely to be seen in the old mountains of the north west of Tenerife. It occurs on this island between Los Silos and Adeje between 300 and 600 m. On Gran Canaria it is found only in the Guayadeque ravine and on cliffs between Agaete and Tirma. It is also extremely rare on La Gomera. It is occasionally used locally as an ornamental plant because of its bluish, divided leaves and red stems. (C.T.G.)

56 PULIDO'S BURNET

ROSACEAE

Dendriopoterium pulidoi Svent.

This burnet is a very local species of the west of Gran Canaria where it is a rare cliff plant. It was not discovered until the early 1970's and even now its distribution is incompletely known. It occurs in the Tejeda and San Nicolas valleys at El Vizo and Pino Gordo. No medicinal properties have been reported and Pulido's burnet is only cultivated in a few specialist botanical gardens. (C.)

57 CHERRY LAUREL

ROSACEAE

Prunus lusitanica L.

This Atlantic species is represented in the Canaries by an endemic subspecies *P. lusitanica* ssp. *hixa*. It is an attractive, white flowered tree of the laurel forest regions of Tenerife, especially in the Anaga forests, Gran Canaria where it is extremely rare, La Gomera where a few individuals occur in the El Cedro woods and in the Frontera forest on El Hierro. The leaves, though poisonous, are used traditionally as an antispasmodic and to make cough medicine. The local subspecies of the cherry laurel is rarely seen in cultivation though the Portuguese form is quite common.(C.T.G.H.)

58 JANDIA RESTHARROW

LEGUMINOSAE

Ononis christii Bolle

Jandia restharrow is a pink-flowered cliff plant from the highest mountain peaks of the Jandia peninsula of the island of Fuerteventura. Its principal locality is on the north face of Pico de la Zarza between 600 and 700 m where it grows with several other local endemic species such as *Argyranthemum winteri*. It is an attractive plant with potential as a garden ornamental. It can be propagated by cuttings or from seed. (F.)

56 | 57
   | 58

59 STICKY RESTHARROW LEGUMINOSAE
Ononis angustissima Lam.

The sticky restharrow with its typical narrow leaves is common in the drier parts of Gran Canaria especially in the south and west, it is rather more local on Tenerife where it is confined to the Guimar area. A succulent-leaved form occurs on the north coast of Gran Canaria on the promentory known as the Isleta. The plant is sometimes used to treat vitamin C deficiency. (C.T.)

60 SHRUBBY TREFOIL LEGUMINOSAE
Dorycnium broussonetii (Choisy) Webb & Berth.

An attractive white-flowered shrub which is native to the islands of Tenerife and Gran Canaria. On the former island this species is locally frequent and occurs in the west and south between Los Silos and the Guimar valley. On Gran Canaria it is very rare with small populations in the Azuaje ravine and on the cliffs of the Montaña del Cedro near La Aldea de San Nicolas. The shrubby trefoil has considerable potential as an ornamental shrub and can be propagated from seed. (C.T.)

61 PINK SHRUBBY TREFOIL LEGUMINOSAE
Dorycnium spectabile (Choisy) Webb & Berth.

This species is a local endemic of the island of Tenerife. It is the only pink-flowered species of *Dorycnium* in the archipelago and has two known populations, one at the Ladera de Guimar and the other in the valleys above Los Silos. The pink trefoil is a very ornamental shrub when in full flower and is a valuable garden plant for subtropical regions. It is propagated from seed and grows best in full sun or partial shade. (T.)

59

61 | 60

62 CANARY BIRDSFOOT TREFOIL   LEGUMINOSAE
Lotus glaucus Aiton

From the central and western Canary Islands and Madeira, this trefoil is a coastal plant usually occurring on rocks and cliffs near the sea. It is very variable in habit, hairiness and leaf-shape and several varieties have been described including an inland form var. *angustifolius* which is locally common on Gran Canaria. Several similar species can be found in the Canaries such as *L. emeroides* from La Gomera, *L. dumetorum* from Tenerife and *L. sessilifolius* also from Tenerife. (C.T.G.P.H.)

63 ANDEN VERDE TREFOIL   LEGUMINOSAE
Lotus callis-viridis Bramwell & Davis

This rare and endangered species is confined to the cliffs of Anden Verde on the west coast of Gran Canaria between Agaete and San Nicolas. It is an attractive groud-cover plant which is easily propagated from seed or cuttings. In its natural habitat it occurs with other very rare species such as *Argyranthemum lidii* and *Camptoloma canariensis* and was only discovered in 1971.(C.)

64 ARINAGA BIRDSFOOT TREFOIL   LEGUMINOSAE
Lotus arinagensis Bramwell

Also a threatened species, this trefoil (previously known as *L. leptophyllus*) is found only on the east coast of Gran Canaria, mainly in the dry coastal region to the north of the town of Arinaga. It forms part of a unique community of coastal plants including *Convolvulus caput-medusae* and *Atractylis preauxiana* which is currently endangered by the extraction of sand in the vicinity. Similar species include *L. kunkelii* from Gran Canaria and *L. lancerottensis* from Lanzarote and Fuerteventura. (C.)

62

63

64

65 MASCA BIRDSFOOT TREFOIL   LEGUMINOSAE
Lotus mascaensis Burchd.

   This small silvery shrublet is endemic to the western end of the island of Tenerife where it is found in the Masca ravine, a locality with many rare endemic species. Its main populations occur on dry, rocky slopes, in open, sunny habitats between 400 and 600 m above sea level. The Masca trefoil flowers profusely in late Winter and Spring and has considerable potential as a garden plant. It is propagated from seed which germinates readily. (T.)

66 HAIRY BIRDSFOOT TREFOIL   LEGUMINOSAE
Lotus holosericeus Webb & Berth.

   A silver, silky-haired species with dense clusters of yellow flowers, this species comes from the southern slopes of Gran Canaria at the lower limits of the pine forests and in the upper limits of the dry zone between 500 and 800 m. It is locally very abundant between the Fataga valley and Pilancones especially along roadsides and forest tracks. No medicinal uses are known but plants are occasionally gathered for forage.(C.)

67 SAN ANDRÉS BIRDSFOOT TREFOIL   LEGUMINOSAE
Lotus dumetorum R.P. Murray

   A local endemic of the island of Tenerife from the southern slopes of the Anaga hills, this species is confined to the valley of San Andrés. It occurs on dry rocky slopes at the upper margin of the dry zone where this meets the *Erica arborea* woodland (500-600 m.). It is one of five yellow-flowered *Lotus* species found on Tenerife and is probably the rarest of all of them. (T.)

65

66

67

61

68 ORANGE DOVE'S BILL LEGUMINOSAE

Lotus maculatus Breitf.

A splendid orange-yellow flowered species which is restricted to a single locality on the sea-cliffs of the north coast of the island of Tenerife near El Sauzal. It is an excellent garden plant which is frequently cultivated locally and is normally propagated from cuttings as seed is rarely available. This plant is a member of a small group of four species all with long pointed petals and a flower structure which indicates that they are probably bird-pollinated. (T.)

69 RED DOVE'S BILL LEGUMINOSAE

Lotus berthelotii Masf.

This is a classic Canary Islands plant which is widely cultivated in warm temperate and subtropical regions of the world (California, S. Africa, Australia etc.) as a garden plant and in cooler regions as a summer patio subject. It is originally from Tenerife where it is almost extinct in the wild. Its natural habitat is on pine forest cliffs on the southern side of the island, though last century it was also found in similar habitats near La Florida on the northern slopes. It is propagated from cuttings as it very rarely sets seed. It has a trailing habit and masses of red flowers. (T.)

70 LA PALMA DOVE'S BILL LEGUMINOSAE

Lotus eremiticus Santos

One of two recently discovered extremely rare endemic species of the island of La Palma, this dove's bill is confined to a single locality on rocks near the north coast at about 300 above sea-level. It has very unusual ochre-coloured flowers with a slight reddish tinge and is an attractive ground-cover plant with garden potential. A second even rarer species was recently found in the north-east of La Palma and named *Lotus pyranthus* after its large, flame-coloured flowers. (P.)

68

69

70

71 CANARY ISLANDS BEAN TREFOIL LEGUMINOSAE
Anagyris latifolia Brouss.ex Willd.

This endemic shrub is a close relative of the Mediterranean bean trefoil (*Anagyris foetida*). Both species are toxic and strongly purgative and the Canary islands plant has some traditional medicinal uses. It occurs in the lower zone between 200 and 500 m. on the islands of Gran Canaria, Tenerife and La Palma and is extremely rare usually growing solitarily or in small groups of a few individuals. The bean trefoil is a valuable ornamental shrub which flowers profusely in late winter. It is propagated from seed which is usually very slow to germinate. (C.T.P.)

72 TEROR BROOM LEGUMINOSAE
Teline nervosa (Esteve) Hans. & Sund.

A very local endemic species of the Teror valley on the island of Gran Canaria, this plant was only discovered in the early 1970's. Its distribution is reduced to a couple of small populations in an area probably once covered by wild olive and mastic woodland. It is an attractive, yellow-flowered shrub which at present is probably only grown in botanical gardens. Like most of its relatives its leaves probably have diuretic and tranquilizing properties. (C.)

73 ROSEMARY-LEAVED BROOM LEGUMINOSAE
Teline rosmarinifolia Webb & Berth.

The rosemary-leaved broom is also a local endemic of Gran Canaria where it occurs on the southern slopes of the island usually in the transition zone between the pine forests and the Euphorbia dry zone. Its silvery leaves and clusters of yellow flowers make it a suitable plant for dry subtropical gardens but at present it is probably only cultivated in botanical gardens. It is propagated from seed and grows quickly into a 2 m. shrub. (C.)

71

72

73

74 LA PALMA BROOM LEGUMINOSAE
Teline stenopetala Webb & Berth.

Locally known as Gacia, this attractive shrub with long spikes of yellow flowers is native to the islands of La Palma, La Gomera and El Hierro where it is usually found at the lower limits of the laurel forest zone. It occurs on Tenerife near Agua Mansa in the Orotava valley but is probably introduced there as a fodder plant. An infusion of the leaves is used locally as a diuretic and as a tranquilizer. This species is sometimes seen in cultivation as a pot plant or as a garden shrub in mild areas. (G.P.H.T?)

74

75 SMALL-LEAVED BROOM LEGUMINOSAE
Teline microphylla (DC) Gibbs & Dingwall

A densely branched, compact shrub with small leaves, this species is endemic to the mountain regions of Gran Canaria where it is very common in open areas amongst the pines and in the cumbres. It was traditionally used as animal fodder and bedding and as a green manure in banana plantations but the natural populations are no longer exploited and have reestablished themselves in recent years. It has the same local medicinal uses as the other brooms and is not usually grown as a garden plant. (C)

76 CANARY WHIN
LEGUMINOSAE

Teline canariensis (L.) Webb & Berth.

This species is often found in cultivation under the names *Genista canariensis* and *Cytisus canariensis*. It is a forest shrub usually occurring in or just below the laurel or Erica/Myrica zones on the islands of Tenerife where it is common in the Anaga hills and Gran Canaria between Teror, Moya and Galdar. It is sometimes cut as animal bedding or as green manure but is still locally abundant. The leaves are said to have diuretic properties. (C.T.)

77 STICKY BROOM
LEGUMINOSAE

Adenocarpus foliolosus (Ait.) DC.

A frequent yellow-flowered shrub of the forest zones especially in pinewoods and on the margins of the laurel forests. The sticky broom, so called because of its glandular leaves and young pods, is found on the islands of Gran Canaria where it is common in the mountain zone, Tenerife, La Palma, La Gomera and El Hierro. It is sometimes cultivated as an ornamental shrub and has a long flowering period from late winter to mid-summer. In the highest mountains of Tenerife and La Palma it is replaced by the following species. (C.T.G.P.H.)

78 TEIDE STICKY BROOM
LEGUMINOSAE

Adenocarpus viscosus (Willd.) Webb & Berth.

From the highest mountains of Tenerife and La Palma, this species is particularly abundant in the Teide National Park on the former island. It is a low, yellow-flowered shrub which differs from the previous species by its very sticky, glandular leaves, pod and calyx and forms typical dominant communities with the white broom or retama and other local endemic species. On La Palma it occupies the upper rim of the Caldera de Taburiente above the pine forests and is the dominant species in this zone. It is not usually found in cultivation. (T.P.)

76

77

78

79 TEIDE WHITE BROOM or RETAMA   LEGUMINOSAE
Spartocytisus supranubius (L.) Webb & Berth.

    One of the best known and most spectacular of all Canarian endemic plants, the Teide white broom or retama is native to Tenerife and La Palma. It is a characteristic plant of the high mountain vegetation of the island of Tenerife. It flowers in late Spring and early Summer and attracts large numbers of pollinating bees and gives a very distinctive aroma and taste to local honey. It is often cultivated as an ornamental shrub in European gardens where it survives moderate winter conditions. (T.P.)

80 TAGASASTE   LEGUMINOSAE
Chamaecytisus proliferus (L.) Link

    This widespread and very variable white-flowered shrub is common on all the islands except Lanzarote and Fuerteventura. It is frequently cultivated as a fodder plant in agricultural zones of the islands and is greatly appreciated for its nutritious value. It has been exported as a forage plant to other parts of the world such as South Africa and New Zealand. The local form from La Palma is sometimes considered to be a separate species (*C. palmensis* (Christ) Hutchinson). (C.T.G.P.H.)

81 WHITE RETAMA   LEGUMINOSAE
Retama raetam (Forsk.) Webb & Berth.

    The white retama is a relatively common species found in the lower zone especially in rocky volcanic areas on all the islands except Fuerteventura. It also occurs in North Africa and the Mediterranean region. This species is particularly abundant on the slopes of the Caldera de Bandama, Gran Canaria and in the valley of Santiago del Teide on Tenerife. (L.C.T.G.P.H.).

82 CANARY VETCH   LEGUMINOSAE
Vicia filicaulis Webb & Berth.

    A scrambling plant usually found amongst shrubs at the margins of the pine forest zone on the southern slopes of the island of Gran Canaria where it is endemic. Its white to pinkish flowers and single or double pairs of leaflets are characteristic. Similar species are *Vicia cirrhosa* from all the islands except Lanzarote and Fuerteventura and *Vicia scandens* with long, many-flowered inflorescences which is endemic to a small area of the north of Tenerife near Agua Mansa. (C.)

	79
81	80
	82

83 CANARIAN BEAN-CAPER ZYGOPHYLLACEAE
Zygophyllum fontanesii Webb & Berth.

This succulent-leaved shrublet is common in many areas of both sandy and rocky coasts on all the islands except La Palma and probably El Hierro. It is also reported from the west coast of Morocco. It is extremely resistant to both dry and saline conditions and is often found within the spray zone on coastal rocks, for example, near the light-house at El Cotillo on Fuerteventura. Because of its rather special ecology it is not usually found in cultivation. (L.F.C.T.G.)

84 CANARY ISLANDS CNEORUM CNEORACEAE
Neochamaelea pulverulenta (Vent.) Ertm.

The Canary cneorum is a yellow-flowered shrub which is locally frequent in the lower zone of the central and western islands where it is found in the *Euphorbia* communities. It is easily distinguished by its trilocular, greyish fruits and linear leaves. The species is said to have numerous medicinal properties and was used by the Canarian aborigenes in the process of mummification of corpses. It is an attractive shrub with considerable potential as a garden shrub for warmer climates. (C.T.G.P.H.)

83

84

85 CANARY ISLANDS CRANESBILL   GERANIACEAE
Geranium canariense Reut.

One of the most characteristic species of the laurel forests of the Canary Islands, the Canary cranesbill occurs on all the central and western islands where it is very common in the Anaga region of Tenerife and the El Cedro forest on La Gomera. It is a large-leaved perennial species with pink flowers of 2-3 cm. in diameter and is often found in cultivation in specialist collections and in botanical gardens. It is propagated from seed and germinates freely. (C.T.G.P.H.)

86 GRAN CANARIA RUE   RUTACEAE
Ruta oreojasme Webb & Berth.

The Gran Canaria rue is a small hanging shrub usually found on vertical cliff faces in the southern sector of the island. Its principal localities are in the the lower zone with other local endemics such as *Prenanthes pendula* and *Convolvulus glandulosus* in the valleys of Tirajana and Fataga and westwards to Mogan and Tazarte. It is easily recognisable by its blue-green divided leaves and typical strong scent. This rue has numerous medicinal properties and is sometimes also grown as an ornamental plant though mainly in botanical gardens. (C.)

87 TENERIFE RUE   RUTACEAE
Ruta pinnata L.fil.

A very tall shrub up to 2 metres, the Tenerife rue is a rare species distributed sporadically in the lower zone between 150 and 600 m. It is found on La Palma as well as Tenerife and a similar species *Ruta microcarpa* occurs on La Gomera. Like most Ruta species it is prized for its medicinal properties but is very rare in cultivation except on La Palma where it is sometimes seen as a garden plant in some of the small villages, for example in Mazo. (T.P.)

88 CANARY ISLANDS HOLLY   AQUIFOLIACEAE
Ilex canariensis Poir.

A small tree which is usually found in the Erica/Myrica woodlands or in the drier extremes of the laurel forest the Canary Islands holly is native to the islands of Gran Canaria, Tenerife, La Palma, La Gomera and El Hierro. It differs from the true holly by its entire leaf-margins though it produces typical holly berries in the winter months. This species also occurs on Madeira where it is rare. It is sometimes cultivated as an ornamental in areas of a mild climate but is rather slow-growing. (C.T.G.P.H.)

89 BROAD-LEAVED HOLLY   AQUIFOLIACEAE
Ilex platyphylla Webb & Berth.

This attractive, small tree occurs on Tenerife and La Gomera and is rather rare on both islands and is only found in laurel forest communities.. It is most likely to be met with in the Anaga forests in the Monte de las Mercedes and at Agua Garcia, both on Tenerife. Though it is not usually found in cultivation, hybrids of this and the garden holly (*I. aquifolium*) have given rise to several of the modern holly cultivars. It is propagated from seeds or cuttings and is slow-growing. (T.G.)

90 CANARY SPINDLE-TREE   CELASTRACEAE
Maytenus canariensis (Loes.) Kunk.& Sund.

A shrub or small tree of the zone between the lower *Euphorbia* communities and the forests particularly in the wild olive and mastic woods which formerly occupied large areas of this zone. It is found on all the islands with the probable exception of Lanzarote though it may yet be located on the Famara cliffs. It is sometimes grown locally as an ornamental shrub and has medicinal properties as a mild stimulant. (F.C.T.G.P.H.)

91 ATLANTIC ISLANDS BUCKTHORN · RHAMNACEAE

Rhamnus glandulosa Aiton

Usually found as a member of the laurel forest community, this small tree is common on Tenerife, La Palma and La Gomera but is exceedingly rare on the island of Gran Canaria. It occurs between 500 and 900 m., and its small reddish-black fruits are greatly appreciated by the forest birds. It is easily distinguished by its small leaves with a slightly toothed margin and the large glands in the axils of the leaf-nerves where they join the mid-rib. This species is not usually found in cultivation but would make a useful ornamental tree for warm temperate climates. (C.T.G.P.)

92 SPINY BUCKTHORN · RHAMNACEAE

Rhamnus crenulata Aiton

This spiny shrub occurs on all the Canary Islands, though on Gran Canaria, Lanzarote and Fuerteventura it is an exeedingly rare cliff-plant. On Tenerife, La Palma and La Gomera it is found in *Euphorbia* communities of the lower zone and is frequent, especially on the northern slopes of these islands. It is distinguished by its small, narrow leaves with toothed margins, its long spines and small, black berries. It is not normally seen in cultivation and has little ornamental value except perhaps as a hedge plant. A third local species of buckthorn is *R. integrifolia* which is confined to the highest mountains and southern ravines of Tenerife. (L.F.C.T.G.P.H.)

93 MOCAN · TERNSTROEMIACEAE

Visnea mocanera L.fil.

The mocan is a Canary Islands and Madeira endemic tree which is still locally abundant in some parts of Tenerife, La Palma and El Hierro, usually in the forest zones, and rare on Gran Canaria, Fuerteventura and La Gomera. Its fruits were used by the original inhabitants of the islands to produce a beverage and syrup and the leaves are said to have medicinal properties. It is sometimes grown locally as a garden shrub and has considerable potential as an ornamental for warmer areas. (F.C.T.G.P.H.)

91

92

93

94 CANARY ISLANDS TAMARISK   TAMARICACEAE

Tamarix canariensis Willd.

A dense shrub with pinkish-white flowers, the Canary Islands tamarisk is common in the coastal regions of all the islands. It is characteristic of places such as El Medano on Tenerife, the dunes of Maspalomas and the lagoon at San Nicolas on Gran Canaria, and the coastal lagoon at Vallegranrey on La Gomera. On the semidesert islands of Lanzarote and Fuerteventura it is typical of the vegetation of dry ravine beds. This species is sometimes used as a hedge plant and to divide fields as well as a dry zone ornamental. (L.F.C.T.G.P.H.)

95 CANARY TREE MALLOW   MALVACEAE

Lavatera acerifolia Cav.

A shrub up to 2m. with palmately lobed leaves which is locally common on cliffs of the lower zone on Gran Canaria, Tenerife, La Palma, La Gomera and Lanzarote between 200 and 600m. Its pale pink flowers with a dark spot at the base of the petal make it an attractive horticultural subject and it is often seen in gardens in warm temperate and subtropical regions. It is usually propagated from seed and has a flowering period of up to 10 months. (L.C.T.G.P.)

96 TENERIFE TREE MALLOW   MALVACEAE

Lavatera phoenicea Vent.

This salmon-pink flowered shrub is one of the most decorative of Canarian plants. It is endemic to the island of Tenerife where it is extremely and occurs only in a few localities between the northern slopes of Anaga and Los Silos. It is deciduous and often flowers on leafless, silvery branches. Despite its potential ornamental value it is rarely seen in cultivation probably because it is difficult to propagate from seed. (T.)

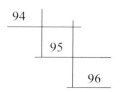

97 CANARY ST. JOHN'S WORT GUTTIFERAE
Hypericum canariense L.

A tall shrub which is common in the upper limits of the Euphorbia zone and in the forest zones of the islands of Gran Canaria, Tenerife, La Palma, La Gomera and El Hierro. Its mass of golden-yellow flowers make it an interesting garden plant and it is used locally in popular medicine. It is very variable in leaf-size and in density and size of the inflorescence and several varieties have been described but in the most recent taxonomic study these are not recognised as distinct. (C.T.G.P.H.)

98 GLANDULAR ST. JOHN'S WORT GUTTIFERAE
Hypericum glandulosum Aiton

This small sticky-leaved St. John's wort usually occurs on cliffs and rocks in the laurel forests and Erica/Myrica woodland where it is locally very common between 500 and 1500 m. It has little ornamental value and is not usually found in cultivation. It is found on the islands of Gran Canaria, Tenerife, La Gomera and La Palma and on Madeira. (C.T.G.P.)

99 REFLEXED ST.JOHN'S WORT GUTTIFERAE
Hypericum reflexum L.fil.

Similar to the previous species, the reflexed St. John's wort is rather more xerophytic in its ecology and is usually found on rocks and cliff-faces in the lower zone where it can be locally very abundant. It is very variable and a number of local forms have been described. It grows on the islands of Gran Canaria, Tenerife, La Gomera and El Hierro and is recorded from La Palma but apparently has not been found recently. It is not usually found in cultivation though it is easily propagated from seed. (C.T.G.H.P?)

100 LARGE-LEAVED ST. JOHN'S WORT GUTTIFERAE
Hypericum grandifolium Choisy

An attractive, large leaved species from all the Canary Islands and Madeira. On the central and western islands it is usually found in forest communities or areas cleared of forest but on the eastern islands it is usually found on humid, shaded cliffs. It has considerable potential as a garden plant though it is not frost-hardy. It is usually confused, in gardening literature with the hybrid *Hypericum X elatum* to which it bears considerable resemblance. (L.F.C.T.G.P.H.)

97

99 | 98

100

101 TEIDE VIOLET   VIOLACEAE
Viola cheiranthifolia H.B.K.

A high mountain species endemic to Las Cañadas del Teide in the central region of Tenerife at 2000m. and above. This tiny violet is found amongst pumice and lava on the slopes of the Pico de Teide volcanic cone. It is locally abundant in a few areas such as Montaña Blanca and grows at the upper limit of vegetation. It is a small, attractive species but is difficult to cultivate because of its special ecological requirements. It can be propagated from seed. A similar, slightly larger species is found in the highest mountains of the island of La Palma (*Viola palmensis* Webb & Berth.). (T.)

102 ANAGA VIOLET   VIOLACEAE
Viola anagae Gilli

This stoloniferous species is a very local laurel forest endemic of the Anaga mountain region of Tenerife. It grows on humid cliffs and mounds in the deepest laurel forest amongst mosses and ferns with another local species, *Tolpis glabrescens*. The original description of this species does not make it clear how this plant differs from the very similar *Viola plantaginea* Webb ex Christ from the laurel forests of La Gomera.It is not found in cultivation though it is an attractive, perennial species. (T.G?)

103 MADEIRA SWEET VIOLET   VIOLACEAE
Viola maderensis Lowe

Sometimes considered to be a local variety or subspecies of the European sweet violet (*Viola odorata* L.), this plant is relatively common in the laurel forest zones of the islands. It also occurs, as its name suggests, on the island of Madeira. Though this form is not common in cultivation, the European form has many cultivars some of which probably involve hybrids with the Atlantic Islands form. (C.T.G.P.H.)

101

102

103

104 GUAYADEQUE ROCKROSE   CISTACEAE

Helianthemum tholiforme Bramw. Nav. & Ort.

An endemic and endangered species of the island of Gran Canaria this plant was originally discovered in the Barranco de Guayedeque where it is extremely rare. Other small populations have also now been located at Pajonales and on the Goyedra cliffs, all in or at the lower limits of the pine forests. The species is not usually found in cultivation though it is relatively easy to propagate from seed. It is a protected species under local and European law. (C.)

105 CANARY ISLANDS ROCKROSE   CISTACEAE

Helianthemum canariense Pers.

This tiny, low-growing plant with pale yellow flowers is found on all the Canary Islands and also on the west coast of North Africa. It is locally very common in dry coastal regions and is sometimes the dominant species in sandy or stony areas near the sea especially in the southern regions of the islands and on Lanzarote and Fuerteventura. It has little value as a garden plant and is not usually seen in cultivation. (L.F.C.T.G.P.H.)

106 MINT-LEAVED ROCKROSE   CISTACEAE

Helianthemum bystropogophyllum Svent.

An extremely rare and endangered species, the mint-leaved rockrose is known only from a single locality in the pine forests of Inagua in the west-central region of Gran Canaria. It is a small, yellow-flowered shrub which has considerable ornamental value as a garden plant and is easily propagated from seed. It has a very close relative, *H. inaguae,* which is also found in the same area but differs by its extremely narrow leaves and technical characters in the flowers and seeds. (C.)

104

105

106

107 CANARY CISTUS or GUM   CISTACEAE

Cistus symphytifolius Lam.

      A common shrub which is indicative of pine forest even in areas where the pines have been cleared. This species is found of all the islands with pine woodlands (Gran Canaria, Tenerife, La Palma, El Hierro) and also on La Gomera where it occurs at the highest points of the laurel forest and fayal/brezal woodland. On Tenerife, on the slopes of the Teide, it also extends down into these communities. it is an attractive species with large flowers. These, unfortunately, last only a single day but an individual plant can flower continuously over several months. The species is usually propagated from seed. An infusion of the leaves is used locally for relieving toothache. (C.T.G.P.H.)

108 CANARY ISLANDS SEA HEATH   FRANKENIACEAE

Frankenia laevis L. ssp. capitata Webb & Berth.

      Locally very common on dunes and coastal rocks, the sea-heath is found throughout the Mediterranean region and extends to southern Britain. The subspecies *capitata* is, however, confined to the Atlantic Islands where it occurs on all the Canary islands and Madeira. It is a small, pink-flowered plant which has little ornamental value and no reported medicinal properties. It is usually propagated from seed. (L.F.C.T.G.P.H.)

109 CANARY WHITE BRYONY   CUCURBITACEAE

Bryonia verrucosa Dryander in Aiton

      A Canary Islands endemic species found on all the islands with the possible exception of La Gomera. This scrambling plant is found amongst shrub vegetation at the upper transition zone between the *Euphorbia* communities and the forests. It is locally very common and is easily distinguished by its palmate leaves and the presence of tendrils. A concoction of the root is used medicinally as a purgative and analgesic though in large doses the plant is said to be poisonous. (L.F.C.T.P.H.)

107

108

109

110 ATLANTIC ISLANDS HARE'S EAR   UMBELLIFEAE
Bupleurum salicifolium R.Br. in Buch

This locally common species is usually associated with cliffs and occurs from the lower zone to the highest mountains from about 100 m. above sea-level on Tenerife up to 1800 m. on Gran Canaria. It is a rather variable, narrow-leaved shrub which is sometimes grown ornamentally for its bluish leaves. It has several local medicinal uses as a diuretic and also to control intestinal gases. In the Canaries it occurs on Gran Canaria, Tenerife and all the western islands as well as on the island of Madeira. A related species *Bupleurum handiense* Bolle is found on the Famara and Jandia cliffs of Lanzarote and Fuerteventura. (C.T.G.P.H.)

111 LANZAROTE FENNEL   UMBELLIFERAE
Ferula lancerottensis Parl.

This spectacular, tall species is found only in the higher parts of the northern region of the island of Lanzarote. It is locally abundant and the leaves when fed to goats are said to improve milk production. On Gran Canaria, Tenerife and the western islands, a second species, *Ferula linkii* Webb, is locally common and a third species *F. latipinna* Santos occurs on the island of La Palma where it is found in the laurel forest zone. (L.)

112 CANARY SAMPHIRE   UMBELLIFERAE
Astydamia latifolia (L.fil.) O.Ktze.

The Canary samphire is a succulent-leaved species which is found on all the Canary Islands and on the Moroccan coast. In the archipelago it is common in the halophyte communities of the coasts of Gran Canaria, Tenerife and El Hierro and less frequent on la Gomera and La Palma. On Lanzarote and Fuerteventura its distribution is restricted to a few localities such as the rocks near the Cotillo lighthouse. The leaves are edible and used in salads, they are said to have a calming effect on the stomach. (L.F.C.T.G.P.H.)

$$\frac{110}{112} \bigg| \; 111$$

113 CANARY CHERVIL   UMBELLIFERAE
Tinguarra montana Benth. & Hook.

A finely pubescent perennial with white flowers, the Canary chervil is locally common in forest and mountain regions especially on cliffs and steep slopes. It occurs between 400 and 1600 m. and is particularly abundant in pine forest communities. It has no reported medicinal uses and is not grown locally as an ornamental. (C.T.G.P.H.)

114 CANARY ISLANDS KECK   UMBELLIFERAE
Todaroa aurea Parl.

Very similar to the above species the Canary keck differs by its winged rather than ridged fruits. It occurs on Gran Canaria where it is rather rare, Tenerife, La Gomera and La Palma, though the populations on this island are rather distinct and may be referable to a new species. It is usually found in lowland communities near the coast below 500 m.No medicinal uses are known for this plant and it is not used as a garden ornamental. (C.T.P? G.H.)

115 GOMERA BURNET SAXIFRAGE   UMBELLIFERAE
Pimpinella junionae Ceb. & Ort.

A local endemic of the island of La Gomera this plant is usually to be found on cliffs in the upper region of the Euphorbia zone and in the forests. It has several near relatives, *P. anagodendron* and *P. cumbrae* on Tenerife, the latter confined to the high mountain zone and *P. dendrotragium* from La Palma and Tenerife. They are not known to have medicinal uses locally but are potentially useful ornamental plants especially *P. anagodendron* with its finely divided bluish leaves. (G.)

113	
	114
115	

116 TREE HEATH   ERICACEAE

Erica arborea L.

The well-known «brezo» of the Canary Islands is an interesting relict species whose present-day distribution ranges from East Africa across the Saharan mountains into the Atlantic Islands and the western Mediterranean region. In the Canary Islands it forms part of the laurisilva and fayal/brezal forest communities usually in humid localities associated with Trade Wind clouds and moisture. It generally occurs in a mixed communitiy in which *Myrica faya* is also present. An infusion of the leaves is used to treat problems of the urinary tract and applied externally to reduce inflamation caused by insect bites. (C.T.G.P.H.)

117 CANARY ISLANDS STRAWBERRY TREE   ERICACEAE

Arbutus canariensis Veill. in Dun.

A rather rare tree of the forest zones of Gran Canaria, Tenerife and the western islands, this species is usually associated with the forest zones both in the domain of the laurisilva and amongst the pines. It is extremely scarce on Gran Canaria and rather sporadic on La Palma. It is an attractive tree with its copper-coloured stems and golden fruits and is sometimes grown as an ornamental. The fruits are rich in vitamin C and are pleasant to the taste. (C.T.G.P.H.)

118 CANARY ISLANDS ARDISIA   MYRSINACEAE

Heberdenia bahamensis (Gaertn.) Sprague

A small tree which is found on cliffs and in the forest zones of the Canary Islands and Madeira. Known locally as «aderno» it is normally associated with the laurisilva communities or the transition zone just below. It occurs on all the islands except Lanzarote though its presence on La Palma requires confirmation and it is extremely rare on Fuerteventura. It is sometimes grown as an ornamental tree and has heavily scented flowers. No local medicinal uses have been reported. (F.C.T.G.H.P?)

116	117
	118

119 TENERIFE SEA LAVENDER PLUMBAGINACEAE

Limonium fruticans (Webb) O.Kntze.

One of about 15 Canarian sea-lavenders, this species is confined to a small area of the North coast of Tenerife where it is found on steep coastal rocks and cliffs.. It is very closely related to *L. arborescens* which occurs in the same area and may only be a local'form. Both are widely cultivated both in the Canaries and in other subtropical regions for the ornamental value of their long-lasting inflorescences and are normally propagated from seed. (T.)

120 MASCA SEA-LAVENDER PLUMBAGINACEAE

Limonium spectabile Svent.

This species is perhaps the rarest of all the Canary Islands sea-lavenders with the exception of the almost extinct *L. dendroides* from La Gomera. It is found only on the inaccessible sea-cliffs of the Masca ravine at the extreme western end of the island of Tenerife. It has potential ornamental value with its divided leaves and mauve flowers but is only seen in cultivation in botanical gardens. It is propagated from seed. (T.)

121 LANZAROTE SEA-LAVENDER PLUMBAGINACEAE

Limonium puberulum (Webb) O.Kuntze

Confined to the floristically rich Famara cliffs of the North of Lanzarote where it occurs between 400 and 600 m., this species is, like almost all the Canarian sea-lavenders, extremely rare. It is cultivated locally as a garden plant and has considerable potential as a warm climate ornamental. It is propagated from seed. (L.)

119
121 | 120

122 GRAN CANARIA SEA-LAVENDER   PLUMBAGINACEAE
Limonium preauxii (Webb & Berth.) O.Kuntze

One of the most beautiful of all the Canary sea-lavenders, this species is locally frequent in some parts of the southern region of Gran Canaria in the Tirajana region westwards and especially in the Fataga ravine. It has considerable ornamental value both as a garden plant and as a cut flower. It is usually propagated from seed as is frequently seen locally in gardens. It has no known medicinal properties. (C.)

123 PINK SEA-LAVENDER   PLUMBAGINACEAE
Limonium tuberculatum (Boiss.) O. Kuntze

Found on the islands of Lanzarote and Fuerteventura where it is a rare species of the North coasts, this plant is common only on the small island of Lobos where it occurs in sandy areas and salt marsh. It used to inhabit similar places in the oasis and dunes of Maspalomas on Gran Canaria but is now, unfortunately extinct at this site. It has inflorescences of small pink flowers and is of some ornamental value. It is usually propagated from seed. (L.F. Lobos, C.)

124 DWARF SEA-LAVENDER   PLUMBAGINACEAE
Limonium pectinatum (Aiton) O.Kuntze

Also pink-flowered, this low-growing species is locally abundant especially on rocky shores and is extremely variable. It is found on all the Canary islands and is often an important member of the halophyte communities where its greyish green leaves are frequently covered with a layer of salt. It is not normally seen in gardens and does not have any reported medicinal properties. (L.F.C.T.G.P.H.)

122

123

124

125 WILD OLIVE OLEACEAE

Olea europaea L. ssp. *cerasiformis* (Webb & Berth.) Sund.

This form of the wild olive is endemic to the Canary Islands and Madeira. In the Canaries it is found on all the islands though it's distribution is now much reduced especially on Gran Canaria and Fuerteventura where it once formed extensive forests. It is a useful ornamental tree and has considerable potential for reintroduction in green-belt areas near the major cities and towns. Various parts of the plant have traditional medicinal uses in the Canaries. The oil from the fruits is used for cooking and as a laxative and an infusion of the leaves, to lower blood pressure. (L.F.C.T.G.P.H.)

126 SOUTHERN OLIVE or PALO BLANCO OLEACEAE

Picconia excelsa (Aiton) DC.

An attractive, small, white-flowered tree with olive-like fruits, this species is native to all the Canary Islands except Fuerteventura. It usually forms part of the laurel forest community or is found on shady, humid cliffs in the lower zone. It is sometimes grown as an ornamental in areas such as the Mediterranean region and California as well as in botanical gardens. It has no reported medicinal uses though it may have some of the characteristics of *Olea europaea*. (L.F.C.T.G.P.H.)

127 CANARY JASMINE OLEACEAE

Jasminum odoratissimum L.

An endemic species of uneven distribution in the Canary Islands, the Canary jasmine is common on Tenerife, La Palma and La Gomera. In contrast, however, it is extremely rare on Gran Canaria and Fuerteventura. It usually occurs in the lower zone and in the transition between this and the forest zones. It is a useful, if somewhat untidy, garden shrub and has no known medicinal uses. (F.C.T.G.P.H.)

125

126

127

128 BROWN-FLOWERED WAX PLANT   ASCLEPIADACEAE

Ceropegia fusca Bolle

An interesting leafless, succulent plant with brownish lantern-like flowers, this species is endemic to Gran Canaria and Tenerife where it is locally common in dry rocky ravines in the *Euphorbia* communities. It is sometimes grown as a garden curiosity and is prized by succulent-plant collectors. The juice is used externally to heal wounds. It is propagated from cuttings and seed. (C.T.)

129 TENERIFE WAX PLANT   ASCLEPIADACEAE

Ceropegia dichotoma Haw.

Similar to the previous species but with greenish grey stems and pale yellow flowers, this species is confined to the north and west of Tenerife where it is locally extremely common (Punta de Teno). It occurs almost from sea-level to the lower forest margins and is somewhat variable in flower size. It is used locally as a garden plant and has similar medicinal properties to *C. fusca*. A closely related species, *C. hians* is found on La Palma and El Hierro. (T.)

130 GOMERA WAX PLANT   ASCLEPIADACEAE

Ceropegia ceratophora Svent.

This is a rare species which is confined to a few localities in the lower zone of the island of La Gomera between 500 and 1000 m. It is easily distinguished by the closed flower-tips and pale greenish-yellow flowers. It is a specialist succulent-collector's plant which probably has similar medicinal properties to the other species of its genus in the Canaries. (G.)

131 KRAINZ'S WAX PLANT   ASCLEPIADACEAE

Ceropegia krainzii Svent.

A second very rare species from La Gomera this is distinguished from the other members of the genus by its dense inflorescences of pale yellow flowers. It is confined to the north of the island in the lower zone up to 600 m. It is reported to have the same medicinal properties as *C. dichotoma*. (G.)

128	
129	130
131	

132 BURCHARD'S CARALLUMA ASCLEPIADACEAE
Caralluma burchardii N.E.Br.

A small, square-stemmed succulent which is confined to stony and rocky volcanic areas of the islands of Fuerteventura and Lanzarote. It is locally abundant but somewhat unobtrusive with its greenish brown stems and brown flowers. This species is frequently found in succulent collections but has little value as a garden plant. It has no reported medicinal properties. (L.F.)

133 BALO RUBIACEAE
Plocama pendula Aiton

A strong-smelling shrub which is common on the dry southern slopes and western slopes of Gran Canaria and rather less frequent on the other islands. The genus *Plocama* is endemic to the Canary Islands and contains only this single species. It is sometimes used for planting along roadsides and has no medicinal properties. Even as a forage plant this species has the disadvantage of giving an unpleasant smell and taste to milk. (L.F.C.T.G.P.H.)

134 CAPITANA RUBIACEAE
Phyllis nobla L.

This is a small shrublet found on rocks and cliffs in the forest zones of the central and western islands and also on Madeira. It is locally very abundant in the forests of Anaga on Tenerife and La Gomera and extends into the more humid pine forests on Gran Canaria. It has no medicinal or ornamental value and is only seen in cultivation in botanic gardens. (C.T.G.P.H.)

135 CANARY MADDER RUBIACEAE
Rubia fruticosa Aiton

A very variable woody climber, the Canary madder is locally common amongst the shrubby spurges of the *Euphorbia* zone of all the islands. There are two forms, one with black and the other with whitish translucent fruits. It is not grown as an ornamental plant but it is known to have several medicinal uses locally. These include improvement of the appetite and use as a diuretic. (L.F.C.T.G.P.H.)

132

136 CANARY BINDWEED   CONVOLVULACEAE
Convolvulus fruticulosus Desr.

A perennial, woody-based scrambling plant which occurs sporadically in the lower zones of Tenerife, La Palma and El Hierro between 50 and 600 m. above sea-level. It is rare on all three islands. The Canary bindweed has some potential as a garden plant though it is rarely seen in cultivation. It is not used in local traditional medicine. Propagation is from seed or cuttings though these tend to root very slowly. (T.P.H.)

137 DWARF SEA-BINDWEED   CONVOLVULACEAE
Convolvulus caput-medusae Lowe

The dwarf sea-bindweed is a threatened species which occurs in a few coastal localities on the islands of Gran Canaria and Fuerteventura. On Gran Canaria it is found in a community with several other endangered local endemic plants such as *Lotus arinagensis* and *Atractylis preauxiana.* It has no known medicinal use but could have potential as a garden curiosity in dry climates. (F.C.)

138 CANARY TREE BINDWEED   CONVOLVULACEAE
Convolvulus floridus L.fil.

One of the most spectacular of all Canary islands plants with its massive inflorescences of white flowers, this species is commonon most of the Canaries and is scarce only on Lanzarote and Fuerteventura. It has enormous possiblities as a dry climate garden plant and is often seen planted in parks and gardens locally. Propagation is from seed. Its native habitat is on cliffs and slopes in the succulent spurge communities where it can reach four metres in height. (L.F.C.T.G.P.H.)

136

137

138

139 FOREST BINDWEED   CONVOLVULACEAE
Convolvulus canariensis L.

A rather uncommon species which is found mainly in the laurel forests of the central islands of Gran Canaria and Tenerife and on La Palma, La Gomera and El Hierro. It has broad leaves and pink-mauve flowers and is an excellent ornamental plant for shady corners in a garden. It is usually propagated from seed though it can easily be grown from cuttings. It is somewhat variable and several local forms on Gran Canaria and El Hierro merit further study. (C.T.G.P.H.)

140 GLANDULAR BINDWEED   CONVOLVULACEAE
Convolvulus glandulosus (Webb) Hallier

Endemic to the island of Gran Canaria this is a cliff plant of the southern ravines of the island where it is locally frequent in the valleys between Santa Lucia de Tirajana and Arguineguin. It is easily recognized by its narrow, sticky leaves and white flowers with radiating pink lines. It is not usually grown as a garden plant and has no reported medicinal value. It grows, however, in interesting plant communities with several other local endemic species. (C.)

141 LANZAROTE BINDWEED   CONVOLVULACEAE
Convolvulus lopez-socasi Svent.

An extremely rare species found only on the Famara cliffs of the northern region of Lanzarote, this bindweed was only discovered in the late 1950's. It is an attractive pink-flowered species which is now quite commonly cultivated as an ornamental plant in the parks and gardens of the island along with a number of other native species. It is propagated from seed and cuttings. No medicinal uses have been reported. (L.)

139

140

141

142 TENERIFE VIPER'S BUGLOSS BORAGINACEAE

Echium virescens DC.

The Canary Islands viper's bugloss species form an exceptional group of shrubs which has its nearest relatives in southern Africa. In the Canaries it exhibits the evolutionary phenomenon of adaptive radiation in a similar way to Darwin's finches in the Galapagos Islands. In all, adaptive radiation has produced about 25 different species in the Canaries. They are some of the most attractive plants and are seen all over the world in gardens in areas with a subtropical climate.

The Tenerife viper's bugloss is found only on the island of Tenerife where it is locally very abundant both on rocks and cliffs in the laurel and pine forests and in the upper reaches of the *Euphorbia* zone. On the southern slopes a very narrow-leaved form reaches almost 2000 m. at the upper limits of the pine forests. This species is sometimes seen as a local garden plant and has become naturalized in California and New Zealand. Like most of its local relatives the flowers of this species produce large quantities of nectar and are visited by enormous numbers of honey bees. (T.)

143 TENTENIGUADA VIPER's BUGLOSS BORAGINACEAE
Echium callithyrsum Webb ex Bolle

Endemic to the island of Gran Canaria, this species is usually found in shady ravines or on cliffs and ledges in the forest zones between 600 and 1500 m. It is particularly abundant at Tenteniguada between San Mateo and Valsequillo on the northern side of the island. This is an attractive species with considerable variation in flower colour from pure white, through various shades of blue and pink to deep red. The blue form is, however, the most common. It is often grown locally as a garden plant. (C)

144 TEIDE BUGLOSS BORAGINACEAE
Echium wildpretii Pearson ex Hook. fil.

Possibly the most photographed of all Canarian plants, the red-flowered Teide bugloss is one of the most spectacular botanical features of the Las Cañadas National Park. On Tenerife it is almost exclusively confined to the highest mountain region above the pine forests but on La Palma it extends into the upper margins of the forest. It has been introduced to the Cumbres of Gran Canaria where it is sometimes seen in flower in the area of Artenara. It is often grown in gardens but does not always flower well at low altitudes at least in the Canaries. It is one of the Canarian plants regularly seen in European botanical gardens. (T.P.)

145 DWARF TEIDE BUGLOSS BORAGINACEAE
Echium auberianum Webb & Berth.

A small, blue-flowered plant which is strictly endemic to the highest mountain zone of Tenerife within the Teide National Park. This is a rare species seen at only a few localities such as the Montaña Rajada, las Arenas Negras etc. and is a protected species. It is not generally seen in cultivation and there are no known medicinal uses for it. (T.)

146 EL HIERRO BUGLOSS BORAGINACEAE
Echium hierrense Webb ex Bolle

This species is a local endemic of the small island of El Hierro. It is relatively rare and its main populations occur in the El Golfo region between Sabinosa in the west and the Roques de Salmor. It is a pink-flowered shrub with considerable potential as a warm-region garden plant and is sometimes seen in private gardens on Gran Canaria and Tenerife. Like all its relatives it is propagated from seen but there is a considerable risk of hybridization if more than one species are grown together. (H.)

143	144
145	146

147 GRAN CANARIA BUGLOSS — BORAGINACEAE
Echium decaisnei Webb & Berth.

A species found on Gran Canaria, Lanzarote and Fuerteventura, this is probably the ecologically widest ranging species of all in the Canaries. It is found from sea-level to the highest mountains and seems to be in flower throughout the year. On the eastern islands of Lanzarote and Fuerteventura it is more restricted and occurs on shady cliffs in the Famara and Jandia regions respectively. Populations from these two islands are considered to be a separate subspecies (ssp. *purpuriense*). (L.F.C.)

148 WHITE BUGLOSS — BORAGINACEAE
Echium leucophaeum Webb ex Sprague & Hutch.

A local endemic of the eastern end of Tenerife on the slopes of the Anaga range of mountains, this white-flowered shrub is locally frequent and can be seen by taking the road from San Andrés to Taganana especially at the upper limits of the shrubby spurge zone. It is not usually seen in cultivation except in botanical gardens and does not have any known medicinal value. (T.)

149 LA PALMA WHITE BUGLOSS — BORAGINACEAE
Echium brevirame Sprague & Hutch.

This species is a local variant of the previous one and is found on the island of La Palma. It is common and very widespread especially in the volcanic regions of the southern tip at Fuencaliente and in the Angustias ravine leading into the Caldera de Taburiente. It is very variable depending on the habitat with an almost «bonsai» form in the windswept lavas of the extreme south. It is not used as a garden plant but, like all its relatives, is easily propagated from seed. (P.)

147

148 | 149

150 GIANT WHITE BUGLOSS   BORAGINACEAE
Echium giganteum L.fil.

The giant white bugloss is a rare species of the northern sector of Tenerife where it grows from sea-level near San Juan de la Rambla to 700 m. in the Orotava valley. It is usually associated with the remains of degraded forest communities. This species can reach almost 3 m. in height and produces large white inflorescences which are extremely attractive for pollinating insects. It is not normally seen as a garden plant but is sometimes used locally in the restoration of roadsides and in parks. (T.)

151 ROUGH-LEAVED BUGLOSS   BORAGINACEAE
Echium strictum L.fil.

A common species on Tenerife, Gran Canaria and La Palma and somewhat rare on La Gomera and El Hierro this bugloss is found in the lower and forest zones. It is easily distinguished by its rather lax inflorescence of blue to pink flowers. Populations with very rough leaves and deep blue flowers found at Buenavista of Tenerife have been described as a separate subspecies (ssp. *exasperatum*) and those from La Gomera are also considered to be distinct (ssp. *gomerae*) A related species *E. handiense* occurs on the high peaks of the Jandia region of Fuerteventura. (C.T.G.P.H.)

152 GOMERAN BUGLOSS   BORAGINACEAE
Echium acanthocarpum Svent.

This robust shrub with lanceolate leaves and deep blue flowers is known only from a few populations in the laurel forests of the island of La Gomera. It is rare but tends to fluctuate in numbers producing large temporary populations following forest fires which are then reduced again as the forest regenerates. It is a very beautiful shrub with considerable potential as a garden plant. It is propagated from seed which germinates freely. (G.)

153 SILVER VIPER'S BUGLOSS   BORAGINACEAE
Echium simplex DC.

This is yet another spectacular Canarian bugloss with a tall, single spike of white flowers. It is confined to a small region of the north-east coast of Tenerife where it is found on sea-cliffs between 50 and 300 m. Locally, in the Canaries, and in other warm climate areas of the world it is used as a garden plant and is easily propagated from seed, flowering in the second or third year after germination. (T.)

150	151
152	153

154 GREY-LEAVED SAVORY   LABIATAE

Micromeria linkii Webb & Berth.

The grey-leaved savory is endemic to the island of Gran Canaria where it occurs in the north and west regions especially from Moya to San Nicolas. It is a small shrub with tiny white or pinkish flowers and is sometimes used in local herbal medicine to control blood pressure. It can also be used as an edging plant in gardens but normally only lives for 2 or 3 years. It is propagated from seed. (C.)

155 HELIANTHEMUM-LEAVED SAVORY   LABIATAE

Micromeria helianthemifolia Webb & Berth.

Probably the most floriferous of all the Canarian savories, this species is found only on the cliffs and rocks of the southern slopes of Gran Canaria. In some places it occurs in large populations but in others only as sporadic individuals. It is easily distinguished by its large, pink flowers borne in terminal inflorescences. It is not frequently cultivated but has obvious potential as a garden plant in drier climates. It is propagated from seed but germination is rather difficult. (C.)

156 WOOLLY SAVORY   LABIATAE

Micromeria lanata (Chr.Sm.) Benth.

A small dense,greyish-white shrublet with pink flowers, this is yet another of the endemic savories of the island of Gran Canaria. It is abundant in the mountain regions and pine forests of the centre of the island. In cultivation it requires well-drained soil and tends to be rather short-lived. An infusion of the leaves is said, locally, to be antiseptic and when taken internally to help regulate the blood pressure. (C.)

154

155

156

157 COMMON CANARY SAVORY   LABIATAE
Micromeria varia Benth.

This is the most common of all the Canarian savories and is found on all the islands and also on Madeira. It is extremely variable and a number of different forms have been described, the most distinct being subspecies *rupestris* from Lanzarote and Fuerteventura. It grows from sea-level to almost 2000 m. but is most common in the forests and in the lower zone. It has, like its relatives, several local medicinal uses. (L.F.C.T.G.P.H.)

158 GLOMERATE SAVORY   LABIATAE
Micromeria glomerata P.Pérez

A very rare species from the Taganana region of the north coast of the island of Tenerife where it is usually found on rocks and cliffs in open communities of spurge and tree-heath vegetation. It is quite an attractive plant with potential as a garden subject for rockeries etc. No specific medicinal uses are reported but this species probably has similar properties to the other Canarian savories. In cultivation it is propagated from seed. (T.)

159 LANZAROTE THYME   LABIATAE
Thymus origanoides Webb

This species is the only thyme to be found in the Canary Islands. It is confined to the cliffs of the Famara Massif in the northern region of the island of Lanzarote where it occurs with several other local endemic plants. Locally infusions of this plant are said to be a mild antiseptic and good for treating chest complaints. It is rarely seen in cultivation but can be propagated from seed. (L.)

157

158

159

160 CANARY FALSE SAGE   LABIATAE
Sideritis canariensis L.

Found on three islands, Tenerife, La Palma and El Hierro, this species is almost always associated with the laurel forest community. It is locally quite common in some places and is somewhat variable. The leaves can range from almost whitish woolly to almost glabrous with glandular yellow hairs. The Canary false sage is rarely seen in cultivation except in botanical gardens.It is said to have healing properties when applied to damaged skin. (T.P.H.)

161 WHITE FALSE SAGE   LABIATAE
Sideritis macrostachya Poir.

Endemic to the forest regions of the north of Tenerife, this species ranges from Anaga to the Orotava valley. It is always found in laurel forest communities where it has a somewhat sporadic distribution. It is an attractive plant with dense, white, woolly flowering spikes and large grey leaves. It is rarely seen in cultivation and no medicinal uses have been reported. (T.)

162 ANAGA FALSE SAGE   LABIATAE
Sideritis dendrochahorra Bolle

A tall, woody species with felty leaves and short flower spikes, the Anaga false sage is also confined mainly to the Anaga peninsula of Tenerife. It is normally found in forest communities but is more xeric in its ecology occuring in the thermophile communities or in tree heath and wax myrtle woodland. It is not used as a garden plant and seems not to have local medicinal uses. (T.)

160 | 161
162

163 RED FALSE SAGE — LABIATAE

Sideritis sventenii Mend.-Heu.

From the dry southern and south-western slopes of Gran Canaria this species is immediately distinguished by the red tips to the corolla lobes. It is known only from a few localities such as the Charcitos ravine and the cliffs of El Viso near San Nicolas. The whole plant is densely covered with white woolly hairs and reaches about 70 cm. in height. No medicinal propeties are reported the species probably has similar characteristics to other Gran Canarian members of the genus. (C.)

164 TEJEDA WHITE FALSE SAGE — LABIATAE

Sideritis dasygnaphala (Webb & Berth.) Clos

The most common false sage on Gran Canaria this plant is found throughout the pine forest and mountain zones often in association with the yellow small-leaved broom. It has several medicinal properties and is used for treating colds and nasal infections and for improving the circulatory system. It is sometimes used as an ornamental plant and is normally propagated from seed. (C.)

165 LOS TILES FALSE SAGE — LABIATAE

Sideritis discolor (Webb ex De Noe) Bolle

Probably the rarest and most endangered of all the Canary Islands false sages, this species occurs as a few tiny populations in the old laurel forest relict communities of the Barrancos de Moya and La Virgen. There are probably fewer than 100 individuals in the wild though it is in cultivation in the Viera y Clavijo Botanic Garden and could be reintroduced to some of its former habitats. It is easily propagated from seed but needs a shady humid habitat for long-term survival.(C.)

163
—
165

164

166 BOLLE'S FALSE SAGE   LABIATAE
Sideritis infernalis Bolle

A very rare species which was, for many years, known only from a single collection from the Barranco del Infierno near Adeje in the south of Tenerife. More recently several more populations have been discovered on shady cliffs in other ravines in the vicinity of Adeje and its status as a distinct species confirmed. It is only seen in cultivation in botanical gardens and no medicinal properties are known. (T.)

167 GOMERA FALSE SAGE   LABIATAE
Sideritis gomeraea De Noe ex Bolle

A spectacular hanging cliff plant from the eastern side of the island of La Gomera, this species is rather distinct from the other Canary islands false sages. It has a long, pendulous spike of flowers with large bracts. The leaves are white-woolly and strongly scented. An infusion of the leaves is used locally to treat intestinal problems. Though not usually seen in cultivation it is easily propagated from seed. Two other closely related species are also found on La Gomera, *S. nutans* and *S. perezii*. (G.)

168 TENO FALSE SAGE   LABIATAE
Sideritis cretica L.

Despite its name this species does not come from the island of Crete, it is a local endemic of the north coast of Tenerife and has a close relative, *S. spicata* on La Gomera. It occurs along the cliffs of the north coast of Tenerife between the Ladera of Tigaiga and the Punta de Teno between 50 and 900 m. above sea-level. Though it is rarely seen in cultivation it is an attractive white-grey species which is easily propagated from seed. An infusion of the leaves is said to stimulate the circulation and can be used to treat colds. (T.)

127

169 CANARY ISLANDS MINT LABIATAE

Bystropogon canariensis (L.) L'Hér.

From Gran Canaria, Tenerife, and the western islands of La Gomera, La Palma and El Hierro, this species is almost always associated with the laurel forests and forest relict areas. It is has a strong, minty smell and like the other members of its genus, is prized locally as a medicinal plant with many applications. It is occasionally cultivated in herb gardens and is usually propagated from seed. (C.T.G.P.H.)

170 BALM OF GILEAD LABIATAE

Cedronella canariensis (L.) Webb & Berth.

A strongly scented plant which is common in the laurel forests of Gran Canaria, Tenerife, La Gomera, La Palma and El Hierro as well as Madeira and the Azores. It is easily reconizable because of its dense heads of flowers and its tri-lobed leaves which are unusual in the mint family. This species is an excellent medicinal plant and a particularly effective decongestant. It is also considered to be very useful as a hair tonic. It is often cultivated in botanic and herb gardens and is propagated from seed. (C.T.G.P.H.)

171 TEIDE CAT-MINT LABIATAE

Nepeta teydea Webb & Berth.

This is a perennial, pink-flowered herb which occurs only in the highest regions of Tenerife and La Palma. On Tenerife it is confined to Las Cañadas del Teide where it is locally common amongst dry rocks and lavas at about 2000 m.. On La Palma it occurs in the leguminous shrub vegetation on the upper rim of the Caldera de Tabouriente. It is sometimes grown in herb gardens and, locally, is used in a concoction for colds and chest complaints. (T.P.)

169

170 | 171

172 RED GERMANDER   LABIATAE

Teucrium heterophyllum L'Hér.

From all the islands except Lanzarote and Fuerteventura, this very attractive red-flowered shrub is sporadically distributed in dry rocky areas in the lower zone where it is sometimes locally abundant. It is of considerable value as a garden plan and its silvery-white foliage can be pruned into formal edging. The aromatic flowers are sometimes used locally to make perfume. Propagation is from seed and the young plants have large, very variable leaves. (C.T.G.P.H.)

173 BROUSSONET'S SAGE   LABIATAE

Salvia broussonetii Benth.

A rare species which is found on the ancient rock formations at either end of the island of Tenerife. In the west its principal locality is in the great Masca ravine and in the east it occurs on the southern slopes of the Anaga peninsula between San Andrés and Igueste. It is easily distinguished by its large leaves and white flowers and makes an attractive garden plant. It is usually propagated from seed. Though a member of a genus with many medicinal plants no such properties are attributed to Broussonet's sage. (T.)

174 CANARY ISLANDS WILD SAGE   LABIATAE

Salvia canariensis L.

This robust, pink-flowered sage is recorded from all the Canary Islands though it is extremely common on some and rare on others. It is a wide-ranging species occuring from the coasts to the high mountains and is very variable especially in the woolliness of the leaves which range from densely white woolly to green and almost glabrous. It is a valuable garden plant though somewhat straggling and untidy and has an infinite variety of local medicinal and culinary uses. (L.F.C.T.G.P.H.)

172

173

174

175 CANARY ISLANDS LAVENDER   LABIATAE

Lavandula canariensis (L.) Mill.

The most abundant and widespread of the Canarian lavenders, this species is found on all the islands except the driest ones, Lanzarote and Fuerteventura. It occurs in the lower zone up to about 700 m. and is usually found on rocks and cliffs in the shrubby spurge communities. Though not as strongly scented as the Mediterranean lavenders this species has a number of medicinal uses and is used locally for treating intestinal worms and as a stomach disinfectant. (C.T.G.P.H.)

176 GRAN CANARIAN LAVENDER   LABIATAE

Lavandula minutolii Bolle

Widespread in the centre and south of Gran Canaria, this species also occurs on Tenerife where it is confined to a single locality on the ridge between Santiago del Teide and Masca. On Gran Canaria it is abundant in several communities from the shrubby spurge vegetation to the high mountain zone above the pine forests. It is not usually cultivated as a garden plant but has similar local medicinal uses to the previous species. (C.T.)

177 PINNATE-LEAVED LAVENDER   LABIATAE

Lavandula pinnata L.fil.

This species has, in the past been much confused with *L. buchii* which is very similar in appearance but which has very branched inflorescences and double-pinnate leaves. It is found on Tenerife, La Gomera and Lanzarote as well as the island of Madeira, usually in dry rocky habitats close to the sea and on cliffs. It is sometimes used as a garden plant for its attractive grey foliage and, on Lanzarote an infusion of the leaves is used to stimulate the digestion and the flowers are said to have sedantic properties. (L.T.G.)

175 | 177
    | 176

178 CANARY NIGHTSHADE　　　　　　SOLANACEAE
Solanum vespertilio Aiton

Endemic to Tenerife and Gran Canaria, this highly endangered species is now found only in a few localites, usually associated with the laurel forest communities. It occurs on the north coast of Tenerife where it is restricted to a few sites in the Anaga forests. On Gran Canaria it is now confined to a single locality between Arucas and Moya. Surprisingly no medicinal properties are attributed to it though it is said to be quite poisonous. (C.T.)

179 GRAN CANARIAN NIGHTSHADE　　　SOLANACEAE
Solanum lidii Sunding

A rare local endemic species of the southern region of Gran Canaria at Termisas, Las Amurgas and Ansite, this nightshade was first discovered in the mid-1960's. It is a shrub of dry cliffs and ravines and has considerable possiblities as a garden plant. It is locally known as wild tomato and its tiny fruits resemble those of the tomato but are not edible. The species was named in honour of the Norwegian botanist, the late Johannes Lid. (C.)

180 CANARY ORVAL　　　　　　　SOLANACEAE
Withania aristata (Aiton) Pers.

The orval is a common shrub of the dry zones of all the islands where it occurs in the shrubby spurge communities and even extends into the forest margins. Though of little value as an ornamental it has a large number of local medicinal uses including being a diuretic, inducing drowsiness and sleep, relieving rheumatism and treating glaucoma. it is not normally cultivated and leaves and flowers for medicinal preparations are collected locally from wild plants. (L.F.C.T.G.P.H.)

178

179

180

181 GRAN CANARIA FIGWORT   SCROPHULARIACEAE
Scrophularia calliantha Webb & Berth.

The most spectacular of all the Canarian figworts, this species is found only on the island of Gran Canaria. It occurs sporadically, usually on humid rocks and cliffs in the forest zones between 500 and 1000 m. Though somewhat delicate in cultivation it has considerable potential as a garden shrub because of its orange-red flowers. Though no medicinal uses are reported many other members of the genus are important homeopathic medicinal plants. (C.)

182 CANARY FIGWORT   SCROPHULARIACEAE
Scrophularia smithii Hornem.

Locally frequent in the laurel forest regions of Tenerife, La Gomera, La Palma and El Hierro and also reported from Gran Canaria where it may be present or has been confused with the European *S. aquatica,* this is a typical figwort with small reddish or green flowers. It has several local uses in popular medicine including treatment of fistulas, dermatitis and shortness of breath. It is grown from seed. (C? T.G.P.H.)

183 GRAN CANARY FOXGLOVE   SCROPHULARIACEAE
Isoplexis isabelliana (Webb & Berth.) Masf.

Usually found on cliffs and ledges in the pine forests this rather rare species also occurs on dry slopes in scrub vegetation on the eastern side of Gran Canaria where it is endemic. It is sometimes found in cultivation though usually in botanic gardens and has mecicinal uses especially as a heart tonic and laxative. It is however, a poisonous plant and should only be used with great care. The bird-pollinated orange flowers of *Isoplexis* are unique amongst the foxgloves. (C.)

182 | 181
    | 183

184 CANARY SEA ROSEMARY   SCROPHULARIACEAE
Campylanthus salsoloides Roth

This species with its nearest relatives in East Africa and Arabia occurs on the Canary Islands of Fuerteventura, Gran Canaria, Tenerife and La Gomera. It has not been found recently on La Palma though it was recorded from the island in the 1920's by Oscar Burchard. It is frequently met with on rocks and lava flows in the lower zone especially associated with the communities of cardón. In cultivation it is quite difficult and requires special care as it is unable to survive excessive watering. It is usually propagated from seed. (F.C.T.G.)

185 CANARY FOXGLOVE   SCROPHULARIACEAE
Isoplexis canariensis (L.) Loud.

A relatively common species on Tenerife and rare on La Palma and La Gomera, the Canary foxglove is generally considered to be a laurel forest species but also occurs in some of the dry ravines of the south-west of Tenerife. It is a medicinal plant «par exellence» and is highly appreciated as a cardiotonic and for reducing the blood sugar content. It is also sometimes grown in warmer climates as a garden plant and is propagated from seed. (T.P.G.)

186 MOYA FOXGLOVE   SCROPHULARIACEAE
Isoplexis chalcantha Svent.& O´Shanahan

The rarest of all the Canary Island foxgloves, this species occurs only in a small area of relict laurel forest on the northern slopes of Gran Canaria between the Barranco de la Virgen and Los Tiles de Moya. It is a strictly protected endangered species which was only discovered and described in the late 1960's. It has rather lax inflorescences of copper-coloured flowers but is not in cultivation except in a few botanic gardens. (C.)

185 | 184
185 | 186

187 CANARY SUTERA SCROPHULARIACEAE

Camptoloma canariensis (Webb & Berth.) O.Hill.

A curious, glandular hairy cliff plant with its nearest relatives in East Africa, this species occurs only on Gran Canaria. It is found on vertical rock-faces in the lower zone of the island between 150 and 700 m., often forming a community of its own without other species. It is very difficult to cultivate because of its very specialized ecology and has no reported medicinal uses. (C.)

188 BROOM TOADFLAX SCROPHULARIACEAE

Kickxia scoparia (Brouss.) Kunk. & Sund.

This small, erect perennial is found on all the islands except Lanzarote and Fuerteventura. It usually occurs in the shrubby spurge vegetation and can be locally quite abundant. It has long, upright, flexible, almost leafless stems and bright yellow flowers with a long spur. The broom toadflax is not usually found in cultivation and does not appear to be of medicinal value. (C.T.G.P.H.)

189 LANZAROTE TOADFLAX SCROPHULARIACEAE

Kickxia heterophylla (Schousb.) Dandy

In the Canary Islands this species is found on Lanzarote and Fuerteventura. It also occurs on the Moroccan coast especially in the southern Sous province with several other Canary Islands plants. It is a creeping or trailing plant which can be found amongst the dry, semidesert vegetation of both islands and has a robust form on the Famara cliffs of Lanzarote (*Kickxia famarae*). A similar species *K. urbanii* can be seen on Gran Canaria especially on the north and east coasts. This species is not normally met with in cultivation. (L.F.)

187
———
189 | 188

190 TIRAJANA GLOBULARIA GLOBULARIACEAE
Globularia sarcophylla Svent.

An extremely rare, dwarf, trailing shrublet from a small area of cliffs in the Tirajana valley of the south of Gran Canaria. This is an attractive blue-flowered species which occurs with several other very restricted local endemics is one of the gems of the Canarian flora. It is rarely seen in cultivation except in a few botanical gardens. A second, also extremely rare species, *Globularia ascanii* is also found on Gran Canaria on the cliffs of the Tamadaba massif on the west side of the island. (C.)

191 CANARY ISLANDS GLOBULARIA GLOBULARIACEAE
Globularia salicina Lam.

This species is common on Tenerife and the western islands of the Canarian archipelago but is extremely rare on Gran Canaria and absent from Lanzarote and Fuerteventura. It also occurs on the island of Madeira. It is a very variable species with leaves which range from linear to broadly lanceolate and spathulate. It is a floriferous shrub and some of the broader-leaved forms have considerable value as gardens plants for warm dry climates. It is normally propagated from seed. (C.T.G.P.H.)

192 TENERIFE JUSTICIA ACANTHACEAE
Justicia hyssopifolia L.

A locally abundant cream-flowered shrub with relatives in East and South Africa, this species is endemic to the Canaries where it occurs on the islands of Tenerife and La Gomera. It forms part of the shrubby spurge community from near sea-level to about 500 m. and is particularly abundant at the Punta de Teno and the ravines in the Adeje area of Tenerife. It is occasionally grown as an ornamental shrub and is propagated from seed. (T.G.)

190

191

192

193 TENERIFE ROCK SCABIOUS   DIPSACACEAE

Pterocephalus virens Berth.

A small, compact shrublet with dense pink inflorescences, this species is confined to a small area of the north coast of the island of Tenerife where it is rather rare and threatened locally by tourist development. It is found on coastal cliffs between sea-level and about 200 m.between Bajamar and the Anaga rocks. It is a plant with considerable potential as an ornamental for gardens in warm climates. It can be propagated from cuttings or seed and flowers profusely in garden conditions. (T.)

194 CANARY MOUNTAIN SCABIOUS   DIPSACACEAE

Pterocephalus dumetorum (Brouss.) Coult.

A very common shrub of the mountain regions of Gran Canaria especially in the Tejeda Caldera and the slopes below Roque Nublo, this species also occurs on the south side of Tenerife in the Güimar valley where it is rather less frequent. Its mass of pale pink flowers and greyish leaves make it an attractive garden subject and it is cultivated locally. It is normally propagated from seed but in the wild, seed production is low due to damage by insect parasites. (C.T.)

195 LA PALMA MOUNTAIN SCABIOUS

Pterocephalus porphyranthus Svent.

Though this species was recognised as being different from its nearest relatives from Tenerife and Gran Canaria by Philip Barker Webb in the middle of last Century, it was only formally named and described in the late 1960's by Eric Sventenius. It is found in the higher mountain regions of La Palma known as the Cumbre Vieja and is locally abundant. It is associated with the plant communities of the upper limits of the pine forests and montane broom scrub. The deep pink flowers make it a potentially valuable garden plant. (P.)

193

194

195

196 FAMARA SHRUBBY PLANTAIN   PLANTAGINACEAE
Plantago famarae Svent.

A very rare species known only from the Famara cliffs on the island of Lanzarote where it occurs between 200 and 500 m. above sea-level. The Famara plantain has two close relatives in the Canary Islands and Madeira both of which are small shrubs with whorls of linear leaves and small, ovate greenish flower heads. This species is not grown as a garden plant and is not used as a medicinal plant. (L.)

197 CANARY ISLANDS RIBWORT   PLANTAGINACEAE
Plantago asphodeloides Svent.

This small, herbaceous annual plantain is sporadically distributed through the south of Tenerife from the Guimar Valley to El Médano and on Gran Canaria between Ayagaures and Mogán. It is found in coastal regions and dry ravine beds from sea-level to about 400 m. Though locally populations can be quite large, they fluctuate from year to year and little is known about the biology of the species. (C.T.)

198 CANARIAN SHRUBBY PLANTAIN   PLANTAGINACEAE
Plantago arborescens Poiret

The most common of the shrubby plantains in the Canary islands, this species is found on Gran Canaria, Tenerife, La Palma, La Gomera and El Hierro. It is usually found on rocks and cliffs in the upper reaches of the spurge zone and in the forests. Though the name arborescence means tree-like it is really a small shrublet rarely reaching more than 50-60 cm. in height. The seeds are said to have laxative and anti-inflamatory properties. (C.T.G.P.H.)

197	196
	198

199 CANARY BELL-FLOWER   CAMPANULACEAE
Canarina canariensis (L.) Vatke.

Endemic to the laurel forest communities of the Canary Islands this species has two close relatives in East Africa. It is one of the best known of all Canary Islands plants and has been adopted locally by ecologists as a symbol of environmental conservation. The beautiful bell flowers appear on vine-like stems in early Spring and are followed by orange, edible fruits. The plants then pass the hot dry summers as dormant subterranean tubers. The Canary bell-flower is often cultivated as a garden or pot plant . It is not used in popular medicine. (C.T.G.P.H.)

200 CANARY ISLANDS GUELDER ROSE   CAPRIFOLIACEAE
Viburnum rigidum Vent.

This splendid white-flowered shrub is one of the most notable plants of the Canary Islands laurel forest community. It is found on all the islands with this type of woodland, Gran Canaria, Tenerife and the three western islands and occurs between 400 and 1500 m. It has the potential to be an important ornamental shrub or small tree and can be propagated from seed or woody cuttings. An infusion of the leaves or fruits is used locally to reduce fevers and as a diuretic. (C.T.G.P.H.)

201 CANARY ELDER   CAPRIFOLIACEAE
Sambucus palmensis Chr. Sm.

One of the rarest of all the Canarian laurel forest species which occurs on Gran Canaria, Tenerife, La Palma, and La Gomera. It is reduced to tiny populations in all its localities and on Gran Canaria only two plants have been located in recent years. On the other hand the Canary elder has numerous medicinal properties including purgative, diuretic and fever control. It is a shrub or small tree up to 5 m. with pinnate leaves and black, subglobular fruits. (C.T.G.P.)

199

200

201

202 CANARY FLEABANE

COMPOSITAE

Pulicaria canariensis Bolle

An endemic species of Lanzarote and Fuerteventura, the Canary fleabane is a rare, threatened species found only in a few localities. On Lanzarote its principal localities are all in the northern Famara region or in the south east and on Fuerteventura in the Jandia region and along the east coast. It is an attractive, grey-leaved shrublet which is used locally in ornamental plantings of local flora on Lanzarote. (L.F.)

203 CANARY SAMPHIRE

COMPOSITAE

Schizogyne sericea (L.fil.) Sch. Bip.

This species is typical of coastal communities in the Canary Islands and is found on all the islands. It is a halophyte which tolerates salt spray on maritime cliffs and is often the dominant species in rocky coastal areas but it also occurs in sand-dune vegetation. An infusion of the leaves and stems is sometimes used locally to heal scratches and minor wounds. It is also sometimes used in roadside and central reservation plantings in dry, semidesert areas. (L.F.C.T.G.P.H.)

204 GLABROUS SAMPHIRE

COMPOSITAE

Schizogyne glaberrima DC.

Endemic to the island of Gran Canaria, this species is a close relative of the previous one and occurs in similar coastal habitats but is probably slightly more drought tolerant. It is rarely seen in cultivation and has no medicinal uses. It is, however, a natural colonizer of disturbed ground, roadsides etc. and many semi-natural populations have been established following tourist development. (C.)

202

203

204

205 FUERTEVENTURA SEA-DAISY COMPOSITAE
Nauplius sericeus (L.fil.) Cass.

Originally endemic to the higher parts of the island of Fuerteventura this species is now widely cultivated as a garden plant in the Canaries and has become naturalized in some places on the north coast of Gran Canaria. It is an attractive yellow-flowered shrub with silky-white leaves and is in flower for almost twelve months of the year. It is an exceptionally tough plant which only requires a minimum of attention. It is propagated from seed. (F.)

206 NARROW-LEAVED SEA-DAISY COMPOSITAE
Nauplius stenophyllus (Link) Webb & Berth.

This species is common in the south of Gran Canaria and also occurs in the Güimar valley on Tenerife. It is a much smaller plant than the previous species and does not have the same ornamental value. It is found in dry open habitats between the valley of Tirajana and Agaete and is particularly common in the vicinity of Mogán and Veneguera. An infusion of the leaves is used locally to treat colds and fevers. (C.T.)

207 SCHULTZ'S SEA-DAISY COMPOSITAE
Nauplius schultzii (Bolle) Wikl.

A somewhat succulent-leaved, low growing shrublet with pale yellow flowers, this species is confined to the islands of Lanzarote and Fuerteventura in dry sandy or rocky habitats. It is a rare species with its principal localities in the north of Fuerteventura between Corralejos and El Cotillo and on the Famara coast of Lanzarote. It appears to be in cultivation only in botanical gardens. (L.F.)

205

206 | 207

208 TENERIFE SAMPHIRE   COMPOSITAE
Vieraea laevigata Webb & Berth.

An important local endemic genus of Tenerife, *Vieraea*, named in honour of the famous Canarian historian and naturalist Don Jose Viera y Clavijo, has only this single species which is confined to the oldest rock formations of the western end of the island. It is easily distinguished by its slightly succulent leaves and its large, yellow flower-heads. It is most frequent on the cliffs at Teno and the valleys south to Masca. It is not normally cultivated but can easily be propagated from seed. (T.)

209 GRAN CANARIA GOLDEN ROD   COMPOSITAE
Allagopappus viscosissimus Bolle

A robust, yellow-flowered shrub of the central and southern regions of Gran Canaria. It is found in dry rocky habitats from the coast to the mountain regions and is locally abundant. Though of potential value as a dry zone garden shrub this species is extremely rare in cultivation. It can be propagated from seed and is a fast-growing, if somewhat untidy plant. (C.)

210 CANARY ISLANDS GOLDEN ROD   COMPOSITAE
Allagopappus dichotomus (L.fil.) Cass.

Somewhat similar to the previous species, this more widespread golden rod has broader leaves with dentate leaves and ecologically is rather more restricted, preferring cliff habitats and crevices.It occurs on Tenerife, Gran Canaria, La Palma and La Gomera from sea-level to about 600 m. and is locally very abundant, particularly in the south of Tenerife. Despite its somewhat aromatic and sticky leaves it does not seem to have any local medicinal uses. (C.T.G.P.)

208

209

210

211 CANARY WORMWOOD COMPOSITAE
Artemisia canariensis Less.

A very common shrub from the lower zones (50-700 m.) of all the islands in the Canary archipelago. Its strong-smelling, silvery-grey lobed leaves make it easy to identify and give it the local name of incienso or incense. It has many medicinal and folk uses including the treatment of worms, water retention, stomach ache and internal gases. It is usually taken in the form of an infusion. It has little value as an ornamental though it can be used as an edging shrublet. (L.F.C.T.G.P.H.)

212 RED EVERLASTING COMPOSITAE
Helichrysum monogynum Burtt & Sunding

Endemic to a small area of the island of Lanzarote this species is extremely rare and endangered with one of its main populations threatened by the enlargement of military facilities on the Famara summits. It is a small shrub with silvery leaves and unusual reddish flower-heads and grows in dry stony habitats in an area with many other Lanzarote endemic species. (L.)

213 LANZAROTE EVERLASTING COMPOSITAE
Helichrysum gossypium Webb

Rather more robust than the previous species, this plant is also a local endemic of the Famara cliffs of Lanzarote where it is rather more abundant. It is found on cliffs and ledges between 200 and 600 m. throughout the Famara massif and the Montaña de los Helechos. In cultivation it makes an excellent grey foliage plant and can be used for edging flower-beds. It has no recorded medicinal uses though its strong-smelling leaves may have similar medicinal properties to other, more common *Helichrysum* species. (L.)

211 | 212
213 |

214 CANARY TANSY COMPOSITAE

Gonospermum fruticosum Less.

A yellow-flowered shrub with divided leaves the Canary tansy comes from the islands of Tenerife, La Gomera and El Hierro. It is particularly common on the north coast of Tenerife and has an isolated southern population at the Ladera de Güimar. It is an attractive late-flowering species which is sometimes used as a garden plant. It also has a number of medicinal uses, infusions of the leaves being used to treat intestinal worms, stomach problems and colds. (T.G.H.)

215 LA PALMA TANSY COMPOSITAE

Gonospermum canariense Less.

A robust, silvery leaved shrub which flowers in late summer, the La Palma tansy is quite common in the forest regions and the lower zone of the island between 400 and 1200 m. It has similar medicinal properties to the previous species and, in addition eating the leaves is said to induce abortion in goats. On El Hierro a local form of this species is sometime separated as a distinct species, *G. elegans.* (P.H.)

216 GOMERAN TANSY COMPOSITAE

Gonospermum gomerae Bolle

From the small island of La Gomera, this tansy is quite rare. It only occurs in the northern region from 50 to 500 m. above sea-level between the Agulo ravine and Vallehermoso where its main population is centred on the cliffs and slopes of Roque Cano. It is similar in appearance to the Canary tansy but can be recognized by its much broader, less divided leaf-lobes. No medicinal uses have been noted. (G.)

214

215

216

217 TENERIFE MAYWEED COMPOSITAE
Gonospermum revolutum (Chr.Sm.) Webb & Berth.

This species is the only herbaceous member of the Canarian endemic *Gonospermum* genus. It occurs only in a small area of the north coast of the island of Tenerife where it occupies the coastal rocks between Punta de Hidalgo and Taganana, Roque Bermejo etc. from near sea-level to about 200 m. It is a potentially useful garden plant but tends to be rather short-lived in cultivation. It sometimes hybridizes with *G. fruticosum*. (T.)

218 SILVER TANSY COMPOSITAE
Gonospermum ptarmacaeflorum (Webb) Febles

This species has been placed, at different times, in several genera including *Chrysanthemum, Pyrethrum* and *Tanacetum*. Recent studies show, however, that its correct position is in *Gonospermum*. It is a rare local endemic of the mountain regions of Gran Canaria where it occurs at the upper limits of the pine forest communities. It is an excellent garden plant but is somewhat succeptible to excessive watering. It is usually propagated from seed. (C.)

219 GRAN CANARIAN TANSY COMPOSITAE
Gonospermum ferulaceum (Webb) Febles

The comments about the systematic position of the silver tansy also apply exactly to this species. It is more common and more lowland in its distribution than the previous species and extends from the Tirajana valley almost to Agaete though the populations on the west side of the island are rather distinct and more isolated from the rest. This species also extends into the mountains at, for example, Roque Bentaiga in the Tejeda region. As with the previous species it has considerable value as a flowering garden shrub. (C.)

217

---

218 | 219

220 LANZAROTE GOLDEN DAISY   COMPOSITAE
Argyranthemum maderense (D.Don) Humphr.

    The original author of this species, David Don in his first publication of this species early last Century, confused its place of origin and named it *maderense*, thinking that it had come from the island of Madeira. It is, however, a local endemic species of the Famara region of the island of Lanzarote. Here it is rather a rare species on cliffs and ledges but, has in recent years, extended its range due to the reduction of grazing in some parts of the Famara massif. It is locally used as a garden plant but has a relatively short if somewhat spectacular early Spring flowering period. (L.)

221 ANDEN VERDE DAISY   COMPOSITAE
Argyranthemum lidii Humphries

    A threatened species which was only discovered in the early 1970's. The Anden Verde daisy is found only on the western side of Gran Canaria in three different localities, Anden Verde, Montaña Almagro and in the Agaete valley. Though originally endangered by overgrazing, this species appears to be recovering and all three populations have many young plants. The Almagro plants which grow in a more exposed habitat have narrower leaves and may belong to a distinct subspecies. (C.)

222 BUENAVISTA DAISY   COMPOSITAE
Argyranthemum coronopifolium (Willd.) Humphr.

    This species, with broad succulent leaves is reported from both extremes of the north coast of Tenerife. It is now, unfortunately, confined to the northwestern end of the island near Buenavista where it is threatened by hybridisation with the much more common *A. frutescens.* The main surviving population occurs in a community with a large number of local endemic species which is one of the richest floristic areas of the islands. (T.)

220

221

222

223 JANDIA DAISY — COMPOSITAE

Argyranthemum winteri Svent.

A very local endemic species confined to the north face of the Pico de la Zarza (700 m.) in the Jandia mountains, this species is one of the rarest plants of the island of Fuerteventura. It is similar in habit to *A. broussonetii*, one of the original Paris daisies, and has considerable potential as an ornamental. It can be propagated from seed or cuttings and survives extreme drought. (F.)

224 MASCA DAISY — COMPOSITAE

Argyranthemum foeniculaceum Webb ex Sch. Bip.

A rather variable shrub with finely divided, succulent, blue-green leaves and large white flowers, this species is endemic to the western part of the island of Tenerife. It ranges from Masca and Tamaimo in the extreme west to Arafo and Adeje in the south and a distinct form which may eventually turn out to be a separate species is found in the high mountains above the pine forests at Vilaflor and the Cumbre de Pedro Gil. The species is quite frequently seen as a summer bedding plant or as a pot plant in European gardens. (T.)

225 MASPALOMAS DAISY — COMPOSITAE

Argyranthemum filifolium (Webb) Humphr.

This is a widespread species from the southern slopes of Gran Canaria where it is extremely abundant in the succulent spurge and dry scrub communities between San Augustín and Mogán. It has fine, long leaves and small flower heads which appear in early Spring. In the west it merges with a similar, broader-leaved species, *A. escarrei* which replaces it between Mogán and San Nicolas. (C.)

226 PARIS DAISY   COMPOSITAE

Argyranthemum frutescens (L.) Sch. Bip.

This species is the most common of all the Canary daisies. It occurs in the coastal zones of all the islands except Lanzarote and Fuerteventura from sea-level to almost 600 m. It is extremely variable and a number of different forms have been described including some which may eventually warrant recognition as distinct species. It was given the common name of Paris daisy as it was first introduced into cultivation via the royal botanical garden of Paris in the 18th Century. Several medicinal properties are attributed to it. (C.T.G.P.H.)

227 HIERRO DAISY   COMPOSITAE

Argyranthemum hierrense Humphr.

An endemic species of the El Golfo region of El Hierro this is one of the rarer species of the Paris daisy group. It is a shrub of the cliffs of the lower zone of the island where it is found in a community with several other Hierro endemics between 100 and 600 m. This species is probably not in cultivation and little is known about its potential as a garden plant or its medicinal properties. (H.)

228 GOMERA YELLOW DAISY   COMPOSITAE

Argyranthemum callichrysum (Svent.) Humphries

Found only on the island of La Gomera where it occurs on the southern margins of the laurel forest zone and sporadically in the northern barrancos, this species is one of only two yellow-flowered Argyranthemums. The species was only discovered in the 1960's somewhat reflecting the state of exploration of the island of La Gomera. It has considerable potential as a garden plant and is easily propagated from cuttings and seed. No medicinal properties are reported. (G.)

226

227

228

229 COLTSFOOT CINERARIA COMPOSITAE

Pericallis tussilaginis (L'Hér.) D.Don

A herbaceous cineraria of the forest zones of Tenerife especially in the north and in the Anaga region where it is very common and from a small area of the pine forests of the Tamadaba area of Gran Canaria where it is rare. This is a variable species in both leaf-size and flower colour. It is rarely found in cultivation but is locally made into a syrup for treating chest complaints such a bronchitis and coughs. (C.T.)

230 WOOLLY CINERARIA COMPOSITAE

Pericallis lanata (L'Hér.) Nord.

One of the first *Pericallis* species to be introduced into cultivation this species is one of the parents of *Pericallis hybrida*, well known in cultivation as the florist's cineraria. The woolly cineraria is endemic to the southern slopes of Tenerife and is also found on rocks and cliffs near Aguamansa in the Orotava valley on the north side of the island. In the south it is locally very abundant between Guimar and Masca in the shrubby spurge zone between 200 and 650 m. (T.)

231 WEBB'S CINERARIA or MAY FLOWER COMPOSITAE

Pericallis webbii (Sch. Bip.) Bolle

Probably the most abundant of all the cineraria species, this plant is found only on the island of Gran Canaria. It occurs from sea-level to the highest mountains and can be found in almost all the plant communities except those closest to the sea and the extremely dry areas of the south. It is extremely variable in size and flower colour. It is sometimes found in cultivation as a Spring-flowering ornamental and is used locally to produce a syrup for treating coughs and colds. (C.)

229

230

231

232 WOODY MAYFLOWER COMPOSITAE
Pericallis hadrosoma (Svent.) Nord.

In direct contrast to the previous species, the woody mayflower is probably the rarest of all the Canarian cinerarias. It is confined to a small area of the island of Gran Canaria between the cliffs of Tenteniguada and Roque Saucillo between 1000 and 1500m. Only a handful of plants still survive and the species has been subject to a scientific recovery programme. It has the largest inflorescences of any member of the group and is a potential source of genes for the production of new forms of the florist's cineraria. Seed production is low and it is usually reproduced from cuttings or by special «in vitro» techniques. (C.)

233 MILKY CINERARIA COMPOSITAE
Pericallis appendiculata (L.fil.) Nord.

A laurel forest species which occurs on Gran Canaria, Tenerife, La Palma, La Gomera and El Hierro, this is the only purely white-flowered cineraria. It is a small shrub of shady habitats and is locally common except on Gran Canaria where a local form (var. *preauxiana*) is found which is extremely rare and almost extinct. A concoction of the stems made with sweet wine and water is said to cure stomach upsets. This species is usually propagated from seed or by offsets. (C.T.G.P.H.)

234 GOMERAN CINERARIA COMPOSITAE
Pericallis steetzii (Bolle) Nord.

Each of the smaller western Canaries has its own local endemic species of cineraria and this is the one from La Gomera. It is a rather variable, and very abundant plant from the laurel forest zone and the upper extremes of the shrubby spurge communities between 600 and 1200 m. It is not usually found in cultivation and no local medicinal uses have been reported. It is propagated from seed. (G.)

232

233

234

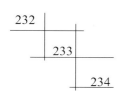

235 CANARY ISLANDS CANDLE PLANT   COMPOSITAE
Senecio kleinia (L.) Less.

A succulent plant superficially resembling the shrubby spurges, this species is found on all the islands in similar habitats in the lower zone. It is locally common and often the principal recolonizer of abandoned and degraded agricultural land. It is sometimes grown locally as an ornamental plant and is also seen in collections of succulent plants. It can be propagated from seed or cuttings and the fresh juice is used locally for disinfecting and healing superficial wounds. (L.F.C.T.G.P.H.)

236 VALLEHERMOSO GROUNDSEL   COMPOSITAE
Senecio hermosae Pitard

One of the rarest of the endemic plants of the island of La Gomera, this species yellow-flowered species with succulent trilobed leaves can be found only in a couple of localities. It was originally discovered on the cliffs of the Roque Cano near the town of Vallehermoso on the north coast and later at Roque Agando in the forest region of the centre of the island. It has no known medicinal value and is extremely rare in cultivation even in botanical gardens. (G.)

237 BOLLE'S GROUNDSEL   COMPOSITAE
Senecio bollei Kunk. & Sund.

From the islands of Lanzarote and Fuerteventura, Bolle's groundsel occurs on cliffs and ledges on the oldest rock formations of these islands. It is found on the Famara cliffs in the northern region of Lanzarote and on the mountains of Jandia in the extreme south of Fuerteventura. It is not usually seen in cultivation and is not used locally in popular medicine. It does, however, have some potential as a dry zone ornamental plant. (L.F.)

235

236

237

238 GRAN CANARIA CARLINE THISTLE   COMPOSITAE

Carlina canariensis Pitard.

This species is endemic to the southern and central region of Gran Canaria where it is locally quite common. It occurs on rocks and cliffs in the lower zone and extends into the southern limits of the pine forest. Higher in the mountains it is replaced by a second local endemic, *Carlina texedae*. The carline thistle has several medicinal uses including laxative properties and as an antispasmodic. It is usually prepared as an infusion of the leaves. (C.)

239 TEIDE CARLINE THISTLE   COMPOSITAE

Carlina xeranthemoides L.fil.

Somewhat similar in appearance to the previous species, this carline thistle has smaller flowering heads and finer, spiny leaves. It is found only in the highest mountains of Tenerife where it is locally very abundant in some parts of the Teide National Park between 1800 and 2000 m. It has similar medicinal properties to the previous species. (T.)

240 CANARY CARLINE THISTLE   COMPOSITAE

Carlina salicifolia (L. fil.) Cav.

The most common of all the carline thistles, this species is found on all the Canary Islands and on Madeira. Is frequent on rocks and cliffs on all the islands except Lanzarote where it occurs mainly in the Famara massif. It is not usually cultivated as a garden plant but is sometimes used as Summer fodder. It is used medicinally as an antispasmodic. (L.F.C.T.G.P.H.)

238
———
240

239

241 CANARY DISTAFF THISTLE   COMPOSITAE
Atractylis preauxiana Webb & Berth.

A dwarf, grey-leaved shrublet which is found in windswept coastal habitats on the eastern coast of Gran Canaria and the south of Tenerife. On Gran Canaria its principal locality at Arinaga where it occurs with several other very rare local endemics, is threatened by port development and mineral extraction and it is already almost extinct on Tenerife. It is only cultivated in botanical gardens and has no known medicinal uses. (C.T.)

242 FUERTEVENTURA SCOTCH THISTLE   COMPOSITAE
Onopordum nogalesii Svent.

This rare local endemic of the island of Fuerteventura is found only in a few isolated valleys of the southern Jandia region. It occurs in very dry habitats in a community dominated by annual species and a few shrubby spurges. It is an attractive purplish flowered species with spiny grey leaves and has some ornamental potential. No medicinal properties are known. This species has a close relative, *O. carduelium* in the Tenteniguada region of Gran Canaria. (F.)

243 CANARY MUSK THISTLE   COMPOSITAE
Carduus baeocephalus Webb & Berth.

A local endemic of Gran Canaria and El Hierro, this species has been the source of some confusion concerning both its nomenclature and distribution. On Gran Canaria it is found on the north coast between Arucas and Agaete and along the west coast to San Nicolas. On El Hierro all its known localities are in the El Golfo region between Sabinosa and the Salmor rocks. It is not used as an ornamental and does not appear to have any medicinal uses. (C.H.)

241

242

243

244 TREE KNAPWEED   COMPOSITAE
Cheirolophus arboreus (Webb & Berth.) Holub

Though not quite as large as its common name implies, this is a tall, robust shrub which is found only on the island of La Palma where it is extremely rare. It occurs only in the Angustias ravine and in a few valleys of the laurel forest zone on the north coast. It is sometimes cultivated in botanic gardens and is grown from seed. Like most of its local relatives in the genus *Cheirolophus* this species probably has medicinal properties. (P.)

245 EL HIERRO KNAPWEED   COMPOSITAE
Cheirolophus duranii (Burchd.) Holub

Similar to the previous species, this plant is a local endemic of the island of El Hierro where it is found in the El Golfo region between Frontera and Sabinosa, on cliffs and rocks in the lower zone. It is occurs on cliff communities with *Juniperus canariensis*. (H.)

246 SVENTENIUS' KNAPWEED   COMPOSITAE
Cheirolophus sventenii Santos

A tall, sticky-leaved species with cream-white flowers, this species is found only in the lower zone of the island of La Palma. It occurs on the north coast of the island between Tijarafe and Barlovento. It is a rare plant which was only discovered in the early 1970's. (P.)

247 TENEGUIA KNAPWEED   COMPOSITAE
Cheirolophus junonianus (Svent.) Holub.

This is also a La Palma endemic. It is found only at a single locality, the Teneguia rock in the volcanic region near Fuencaliente. In this locality the plant is quite common and occurs in both pinnate and entire-leaved forms but because of the very reduced area of the Teneguia rock it must be considered to be an endangered species. (P.)

244	245
246	

247

248 GÜI GÜI KNAPWEED   COMPOSITAE

Cheirolophus falcisectus (Svent.) Montel.& Moral.

This local Gran Canaria endemic occurs only at Artejeve in the Güi Güi mountains between the Aldea de San Nicolas and Veneguera. It is extremely rare and is found on shady cliffs at about 600 m. above sea-level. It is cultivated in botanical gardens and forms an attractive purplish-flowered shrub. (C.)

249 TENO KNAPWEED   COMPOSITAE

Cheirolophus canariensis (Willd.) Holub

From the western end of Tenerife, this species occurs in two forms which should, perhaps, be recognised as separate species. The typical form with pinnate leaves is found in the Masca ravine and the illustrated form is from the sea-cliffs between Buenavista and the Punta de Teno where it is quite frequent. This form has subentire leaves and grows in a cummunity rich in local endemic species. It has several medicinal properties such as the lowering of blood sugar levels and as an antibiotic. Its juice is also said to prevent cell division in tumours. (T.)

250 AGAETE KNAPWEED   COMPOSITAE

Cheirolophus arbutifolius (Svent.) Holub

This tall, entire-leaved species has deep pink flowers. It is found sparingly at several localities in the north and north-west of Gran Canaria from Tenteniguada to the San Nicolas valley. It usually occurs on ancient cliffs between 400 and 800 m. It is one of the most attractive species of the group and is often used locally as a garden shrub and as a medicinal plant with similar properties to the previous species and is usually propagated from seed. (C.)

248 | 249
250 |

251 CANARY WALL LETTUCE   COMPOSITAE
Tolpis lagopoda Chr.Sm.

A forest-dwelling species which is found on the islands of Gran Canaria, Tenerife and La Palma, this is a common plant in both the laurisilva and pine communities of Tenerife and is rather more rare on Gran Canaria and its presence on La Palma has not been confirmed recently. It has several relatives in the Islands including the more widespread *T. laciniata* and the high mountain species *T. webbii* which is confined to the central region of Tenerife. (C.T.P.)

252 CANARY MOUSE-EAR   COMPOSITAE
Andryala pinnatifida Aiton

A common species found in shady places, in forests and cliffs etc. on all the islands. It is particularly common in the laurel forests especially in open areas, roadsides and clearings and in the pine forests of Tenerife. This species is extremely variable and several varieties are recognised. A very distinct form from the north of La Palma has been considered to be a distinct species, *A. webbii*. No medicinal properties are reported. (L.F.C.T.G.P.H.)

253 TENO CAT'S EAR   COMPOSITAE
Hypochaeris oligocephala (Svent.& Bramw.) Lack

One of the rarest of all Canary Island plants, this species is found only on a single face of the cliffs of El Fraile between Buenavista and Teno at the north-west extreme of Tenerife. There are many other very restricted local endemics to be seen in the same area making it one of the most botanically important localities in the archipelago. It is an isolated species which has no obviously related species in the genus *Hypochaeris*. (T.)

$$252 \ \begin{array}{|l} 251 \\ \hline 253 \end{array}$$

254 DON ENRIQUE'S SOW-THISTLE — COMPOSITAE
Sventenia bupleuroides Font Quer

Also a very rare plant in a genus of its own this species is confined to the north and west cliff-faces of the Tamadaba mountain on Gran Canaria. It occurs along the upper border of the cliffs and in shady ravines between the Agaete valley and the Faneque outcrop. It is a plant of the humid pine forest zone and is found between 600 and 800 m. often in the company of other endemics such as *Dendriopoterium menendezii*. (C.)

255 GRAN CANARY MOUNTAIN LETTUCE — COMPOSITAE
Prenanthes pendula (Webb) Sch. Bip.

A frequent cliff species in the southern regions of Gran Canaria between the Tirajana valley and Agaete, this is a problematical plant which may not be a true member of the genus *Prenanthes*. It is a trailing, woody-based shrub which often occurs with other cliff plants such as *Convolvulus glandulosus* and *Micromeria helianthemifolia*. It is particularly common in the Fataga ravine where there are plants with woody stems of up to 3 m. in length. (C.)

256 CANARY ISLANDS HAWK'S BEARD — COMPOSITAE
Crepis canariensis (Sch.Bip.) Babcock

This species occurs only on the two eastern islands of Lanzarote and Fuerteventura. On Lanzarote it is common in the northern region especially in the Famara massif where it occurs on cliffs from near sea-level to 600 m. On Fuerteventura it is found in various localities but always in shady habitats on old mountain blocks. It is particularly common on the steep cliff-face of Pico de la Zarza on the Jandia peninsula. It is not usually found in cultivation. (L.F.)

254

255

256

257 LA PALMA SOW-THISTLE   COMPOSITAE
Sonchus palmensis (Sch. Bip.) Boulos

A tall shrub up to 3 m. which produces masses of yellow flowers in Spring, this species is endemic to the island of La Palma where it is common in the mid-zones and laurel forest communities in the northern part. It is grown locally as an ornamental and also as a forage plant which is said to increase milk production. (P.)

258 FENNEL-LEAVED SOW-THISTLE   COMPOSITAE
Sonchus leptocephalus Cass.

This delicate shrub with small flowers and finely divided leaves is an extemely common species on walls, rocks and cliffs in the lower zones of Tenerife and Gran Canaria. It is reported from Fuerteventura (Montaña de Cardones) but records from La Gomera probably refer to *Sonchus filifolius*. It is not normally grown as a garden plant and grazing animals usually eat only the flowers. (F.C.T.)

259 FRONTERA SOW-THISTLE   COMPOSITAE
Sonchus gandogeri Pitard

A very rare endemic of the island of El Hierro, the Frontera sow-thistle occurs on the cliffs of El Golfo below the laurel forests and also on the coastal cliffs of the eastern side of the island between Valverde and La Restinga. It sometimes hybridizes with *Sonchus hierrense* in the Frontera region and the hybrids are often used as forage plants. (H.)

260 VALLEHERMOSO SOW-THISTLE   COMPOSITAE
Sonchus regis-jubae Pitard

Locally frequent in the Vallehermoso region of La Gomera, this north-coast species is endemic to the island. Records from other islands seem to refer to hybrids of *S. leptocephalus* with broader-leaved species or to *S. arboreus* as in the case of reports from La Palma. It occurs in the lower zone in communities with *Globularia salicina* and the shrubby spurges and in open habitats with *Juniperus canariensis*. (G.)

257	258
259	260

261 GIANT CANARY SOW-THISTLE COMPOSITAE
Sonchus canariensis (Sch.Bip.) Boulos

The most spectacular of all the Canarian sow-thistles, this species can grow to over 3 m. in height. It is found on Gran Canaria and Tenerife. On the former it occurs in the laurel forest zone at Moya and in the lower zone at Anden Verde and on the slopes on the north side of the barranco de San Nicolas. In this area it is usually found closely associated with the cardón (*Euphorbia canariensis*). It is rare on Tenerife and occurs sporadically in the southern barrancos between Güimar and Adeje. It is rare in cultivation and is propagated from seed. (C.T.)

262 FAMARA SOW-THISTLE COMPOSITAE
Sonchus pinnatifidus Cav.

In the Canary islands this species grows on the islands of Lanzarote and Fuerteventura. It is also found in Morocco, though a revision of plants from both areas may lead to their separation as two distinct species. On Lanzarote it occurs on the Famara cliffs and on Fuerteventura at Montaña Cardones and the northern part of Jandia. It is not grown as an ornamental plant and no medicinal uses are known. (L.F.)

263 TREE SOW-THISTLE COMPOSITAE
Sonchus arboreus DC.

A tall shrub which scarcely merits the name «arboreus», this species comes from Tenerife where it is found in the north west,particularly on the slopes of Punta de Teno and on La Palma where it is found in the north and north west of the island. It grows in the lower zone from 100 to 300 m. and, on Tenerife, is usually found amongst clumps of *Euphorbia canariensis*. It is extremely rare in cultivation and is probably only to be seen in a few botanical gardens. (T.P.)

261

262

263

264 TUBEROUS SOW-THISTLE   COMPOSITAE

Sonchus radicatus Aiton

A locally common species from the north coast of Tenerife between the Anaga point and the Teno cliffs, this plant is found on cliffs in the lower zone between sea-level and 400 m. It is an attractive , floriferous species with grey pinnate leaves but is not usually grown as a garden plant. It can be propagated from its tuberous roots or from seed. (T.)

265 GRAN CANARY SOW-THISTLE   COMPOSITAE

Sonchus brachylobus Webb & Berth.

This species is frequent along the north coast of Gran Canaria and on the west coast to San Nicolas. It is a small shrub with rounded leaf-lobes and is found on cliffs and rocks in the coastal and Euphorbia zones. It is quite variable and on the west side of the island populations with pointed rather than rounded lobes have been described as a distinct species, *S.canariae* but probably only merit being separated as a local variety. (C.)

266 GOMERA SOW-THISTLE   COMPOSITAE

Sonchus gonzalez-padronii Svent.

The Gomera sow-thistle is a species from the coastal regions of La Gomera. It is similar to *S. radicatus* in habit and ecology and has been considered by some experts to be a subspecies of it. It occurs sporadically along the north coast from San Sebastian to Vallehermoso and also from Epina to the Argaga ravine, Vallegranrey and the Fortaleza mountain at Chipude. It is probably not in cultivation except in botanical gardens. (G.)

264

265 | 266

267 ANAGA SOW-THISTLE

COMPOSITAE

Sonchus congestus Willd.

This robust shrub occurs on the two islands of Gran Canaria and Tenerife. On the first it is a rather uncommon species which is found in the remains of the laurel forests in the Moya region. On Tenerife, however, it is a very common species which is distributed from the Anaga forest region along the north coast to Buenavista and Teno between 500 and 1500 m. above sea-level. The leaves are sometimes used for forage and are said to improve milk productivity and quality. (C.T.)

268 BORNMUELLER'S SOW-THISTLE

COMPOSITAE

Sonchus bornmuelleri Pitard

A rare species of the island of La Palma where it is sporadically distributed along the east coast and the north and north-west from Garafia to Fuencaliente. It is found on coastal cliffs and is tolerant of salt spray and maritime influence in its habitat. It is rarely seen in cultivation and no medicinal or other uses are known .This species is easily distinguished form all the other Canarian sow-thistles by its rounded leaf-lobes. (P.)

269 STEMLESS SOW-THISTLE

COMPOSITAE

Sonchus acaulis Dum.Cours.

This is probably the most widely distributed of all the Canary sow-thistles. It occurs on Gran Canaria and Tenerife and is found from the coasts to the highest mountains between 100 and 1800 m. The stemless sow-thistle can be found amongst the shrubby spurges, on forest cliffs in the laurel woodlands or in the pine forests and in the high mountain shrubland with brooms and sage. It is an unbranched rosette plant which produces a large inflorescence in late Spring. (C.T.)

267

268 | 269

270 ORTUÑO'S SOW-THISTLE COMPOSITAE

Sonchus ortunoi Svent.

From the central and south-western part of La Gomera, this local endemic species is rather uncommon. It is a shrub of cliffs and rocks in the lower zone, juniper shrubland and laurel forest margins. The leaves are sometimes collected for forage but no medicinal properties have been reported. The species is rarely seen in cultivation. (G.)

271 LITTLE SOW-THISTLE COMPOSITAE

Sonchus tuberifer Svent.

This species is a small herb which grows in rock crevices on the western mountains of Tenerife. It can be found in the area between Buenavista, Masca and Tamaimo at an altitude of 150-1000 m. It is sporadic in its distribution and is nowhere common. It is a perennial species with a tuberous root which is deeply wedged into cracks and crevices on the old basalt rocks of the region. (T.)

272 NUBLO SOW-THISTLE COMPOSITAE

Sonchus platylepis Webb & Berth.

An unusual sow-thistle with grey-waxy leaves and very large flower-heads, this species is endemic to the mountain regions and pine forests of the island of Gran Canaria where it is locally abundant between 800 and 1600 m. Though rarely seen as an ornamental, this species has considerable possiblities as a garden plant. It is sometimes placed in a separate genus *Babcockia*, but the diversity found in the Canarian species of the genus *Sonchus* is so great that the splitting off of a few species seems unwarranted. (C.)

270

271

272

273 SPINY LETTUCE or BARBED-WIRE BUSH   COMPOSITAE
Launaea arborescens (Batt.) Murb.

A common shrub of lowland and semidesert areas of all the Islands, this species also occurs in the Mediterranean region and North Africa. In the Canaries it forms the dominant vegetation in the driest regions and is especially abundant on Fuerteventura and areas of the south of Gran Canaria and Tenerife. Infusions of the flowers are used as a tonic and in local folk medicine, to cure jaundice. It can be truly said of this plant that it has no ornamental value. (L.F.C.T.G.P.H.)

274 TENERIFE SEA-HAWKBIT   COMPOSITAE
Reichardia crystallina (Sch.Bip.) Bramwell

A locally frequent rosette plant with slightly succulent, papillate leaves, this species occurs on rocky coasts of the south of Tenerife in the vicinity of the Güimar valley and in the north near Buenavista and Teno. On the other islands it is usually replaced by a similar species *R. ligulata* with larger, branched inflorescences. (T.)

275 FAMARA HAWKBIT   COMPOSITAE
Reichardia famarae Bramwell & Kunkel

This large-leaved plant is a local endemic of the cliff regions of Famara on Lanzarote and the Jandia peaks on Fuerteventura. It is rare but locally there are large populations at Mirador del Rio on Lanzarote and Pico de La Zarza on Fuerteventura. This species is rarely seen in cultivation though it is sometimes used locally on Lanzarote in plantings of native species. (L.F.)

273

274

275

276 DRAGON TREE LILIACEAE
Dracaena draco L.

One of the best known and most widely cultivated of all Canary islands plants, the dragon tree is encountered in parks and gardens throughout the warm temperate and subtropical world. It is a slow-growing tree of cliffs in the lower zone of the islands and has its main natural populations on Tenerife, La Palma and Gran Canaria. Isolated individuals are also present on inaccessible cliffs of La Gomera and El Hierro. The dragon tree also occurs on Madeira and the Cape Verde Islands. Its sap, dragon's blood, is used as a dye and in making varnish and medicinally for strengthening the gums, an infusion of the fruits is used as cough medicine. (C.T.P.G.H.)

277 CLIMBING BUTCHER'S BROOM LILIACEAE
Semele androgyna (L.) Kunth.

This is a robust climber which is found on Gran Canaria, Tenerife, La Palma, La Gomera and El Hierro. It occurs in the laurel forests and is locally quite frequent. The form from Gran Canaria is sometimes considered to be a distinct variety but hardly merits formal recognition as the charcters of flower position used to separate it overlap in populations of the different islands. It is often grown as a garden plant especially on Tenerife and La Palma. The roots and stems are used in local medicine as a diuretic. (C.T.G.P.H.)

278 SPINY SMILAX LILIACEAE
Smilax aspera L.

A scrambling, leafy herb of the laurel forest zones of Gran Canaria and the western islands. This species has a large number of local medicinal uses such as to induce sweating during fevers, as a diuretic, and for lowering blood-sugar levels. Preparations are usually made in the form of infusions of the roots and fresh leaves. It is also occasionally grown as an ornamental pot plant. (C.T.G.P.H.)

199

279 CANARY SMILAX LILIACEAE
Smilax canariensis Willd.

From the islands of Tenerife, La Palma and La Gomera, this local endemic species is also a laurel forest species though it is also occasionally found in humid pine forests and at the upper reaches of the shrubby spurge zone on shady cliffs. It has similar medicinal properties to the previous species from which it is distinguished by its spineless leaf margins. (T.P.G.)

280 CANARY BLACK BRYONY DIOSCOREACEAE
Tamus edulis Lowe

The Canary bryony is found on all the islands except Lanzarote and also on Madeira. It is a common species in the upper reaches of the spurge zone especially on shady cliffs and amongst dense shrub vegetation. The roots are said to be edible and the plant was apparently cultivated for food on Madeira during the last Century. Preparations of the roots are also used locally for treatment of circulatory problems, to treat rheumatism and against allergies. It is generally applied externally. (F.C.T.G.H.P.)

281 CANARY SEA-DAFFODIL AMARYLLIDACEAE
Pancratium canariensis Ker.Gawl.

This attractive, white-flowered plant occurs on all the Islands. It is quite common in some areas of the lower zone on cliffs and ledges in the *Euphorbia* communities. Unfortunately,it has only a very short flowering period in late Autumn. A second sea-daffodil, *P. maritimum* is found on Fuerteventura, in the sand dunes at Corralejo where it is rather rare. (L.F.C.T.G.P.H.)

279

| 280 | 281 |

282 CANARY SQUILL   LILIACEAE
Scilla latifolia Willd.

One of the most beautiful of all the squills, this species is found on all the Canary Islands with the probable exception of Lanzarote. It is sporadic in its distribution and is usually found near the coast in the shrubby spurge zone. It is rare on Gran Canaria and its survival on this island has only recently been confirmed. The bulbs of this species contain glycosides and the plant is rather poisonous though it may have medicinal uses to control heart problems but under strict medical supervision. It is occasionally grown as an ornamental pot-plant. (L.F.C.T.G.P.H.)

283 LESSER CANARY SQUILL   LILIACEAE
Scilla haemorrhoidalis Webb & Berth.

This tiny species with long, linear to lanceolate leaves is found on all the Canary islands. It is locally frequent in the lower zone and occasionally extends into the cliff areas of the laurel woodlands. It bulbs have similar properties to those of *S. latifolia* and are also toxic. The lesser Canary squill is not seen in cultivation as it has a very short flowering period and a rather lax, depauperate inflorescence. (L.F.C.T.G.P.H.)

282

283

284 CANARY ISLANDS DATE PALM   PALMAE
Phoenix canariensis Chabaud

The Canary Islands date palm is one of the most typical plants of the Canarian landscape. It is a tall, majestic tree which forms large groves in the beds of many ravines. It occurs on all the islands and has several outstanding localities such as Sorueda and the Fataga valley on Gran Canaria, Haria on Lanzarote and Vallehermoso and Vallegranrey on La Gomera. This tree has many uses including the extraction of syrup (guarapo) from the tip of the trunk and the leaf fibre for making all types of baskets and other handicraft. It is widely cultivated in warmer climates throughout the world and is the official botanical symbol of the Canary islands. (L.F.C.T.G.P.H.)

285 SAND CROCUS   LILIACEAE
Androcymbium psammophilum Svent.

A tiny ephemeral plant found only in sand dune regions of Lanzarote and Fuerteventura where it is rare. It flowers briefly in late Winter and by the end of Spring has disappeared completely to pass the dry summer as a dormant bulb below the ground. It is known only from the Corralejo dunes on Fuerteventura and the Caleta de Famara on Lanzarote. (L.F.)

286 CANARY ROMULEA   IRIDACEAE
Romulea columnae Seb.& Maur. var. *grandiscapa* Gay.

A small crocus-like plant which is found on all the Canary islands from the lower zones to the forests. It is particularly frequent in pine woodlands. The genus *Romulea* is a difficult one and its representative(s) in the Canaries are no exception, several forms, varieties and even distinct species having been described. It is an attractive pinkish flowered plant but is not grown as an ornamental and no medicinal uses are recorded. (L.F.C.T.G.P.H.)

284

285

286

287 TREE ASPARAGUS LILIACEAE

Asparagus arborescens Willd.

    This tall shrub is commonly found in the shrubby spurge communities of Gran Canaria and Tenerife and is rather more rare on La Gomera where it only occurs in a small area of the north coast. The young shoots are sometimes collected and eaten as *Asparagus* tips and the plant is often grown locally as a foliage ornamental. (C.T.G.)

288 WEEPING ASPARAGUS LILIACEAE

Asparagus plocamoides (Bolle) Svent.

    Like the previous species in habit but with long, graceful, weeping branches, this plant is rather rare. It occurs only on Gran Canaria, Tenerife and La Palma. It is found on cliffs and ledges usually in the forest areas, especially in the pines of Tenerife between 1000 and 2000 m. and at the transition between the laurel forest and pine zones on Gran Canaria. A close relative, *A. scoparius* is also found on the same three islands. (C.T.P.)

289 UMBELLATE ASPARAGUS LILIACEAE

Asparagus umbellatus Link

    A climbing shrub which is found on Gran Canaria, Tenerife and the western islands. It occurs throughout the lower, spurge zone and also in the laurel forests and is probably the most common Canarian *Asparagus*. In drier region it sometimes occurs together with *A. pastorianus* which is a more robust, spiny species. The rhizomes and stems are used for making an infusion which is said to have a strong diuretic effect. (C.T.G.P.H.)

290 SEA ASPARAGUS LILIACEAE

Asparagus nesiotes Svent.

    On Lanzarote and Fuerteventura, *A. umbellatus* is replaced in the shrubby spurge communities by this species which is also found on the Salvage Islands between the Canaries and Madeira. it is locally very common in some areas such as the north coast of Jandia on Fuerteventura and the Malpais de la Corona on Lanzarote. (L.F.)

288	
289	287
290	

291 CANARY ISLANDS HAIR-GRASS　　GRAMINAE
Tricholaena teneriffae (L.fil.) Link

This species is very common on all the Islands where it is usually found in the lower zone. It occurs on dry slopes and in volcanic debris and is easily distinguished by its delicate inflorescences. it is sometimes grazed by goats but does not seem to be a particularly palatable species. (L.F.C.T.G.P.H.)

292 CANARY ISLANDS FALSE BROME　　GRAMINAE
Brachypodium arbusculum Gay ex Knoche

An endemic grass from the rocks and cliffs of the lower zone on the north west coast of Tenerife and from the north of La Gomera and El Hierro. This is a robust species, rather larger than the other species of false brome and is sometimes used locally as a forage species. it is locally abundant but rather restricted in its distribution. (T.G.H.)

293 CANARY COCKSFOOT　　GRAMINAE
Dactylis smithii Link

A dense, tufted cocksfoot known from all the Canary Islands except Fuerteventura and from Madeira. It is sporadically distributed from the coast to the high mountains and is extremely variable and in need of systematic study. it has considerable potential as a dry zone forage grass. (L.C.T.G.P.H.)

294 CANARY ISLANDS FESCUE　　GRAMINAE
Festuca agustini Lindinger

A species of humid habitats and forest zones from 400 to 1600 m. the Canary fescue is found on Gran Canaria, Tenerife, La Palma, La Gomera and El Hierro. It is particularly abundant in the forest regions of La Palma. It is not locally used as forage and no medicinal properties have been recorded. (C.T.G.P.H.)

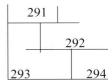

295 TWO-LEAVED ORCHID   ORCHIDACEAE
Gennaria diphylla Parl.

A small easily identified orchid which usually occurs on the cliffs of the laurel-forest zone and extends into the more humid pine forests. It occurs on Gran Canaria, Tenerife and the western islands aand is also distributed through North Africa and south-west Europe. (C.T.G.P.H.)

296 CANARY ISLANDS PURPLE ORCHID   ORCHIDACEAE
Orchis canariensis Lindl.

This pink-purple flowered orchid is found in the upper part of the *Euphorbia* zone especially in shady places and in the pine forests. It comes from Gran Canaria, Tenerife, La Palma, La Gomera and El Hierro. A second *Orchis* species, *O. mascula* which is a Mediterranean species is also found on La Palma in pine woodland. (C.T.G.P.H.)

297 CANARY TWAYBLADE   ORCHIDACEAE
Habenaria tridactylites Lindl.

An inconspicuous, green-flowered species which is found on shady rocks in the lower and forest zones of all the islands except Lanzarote and Fuerteventura. In some places it can be exceptionally abundant especially on Gran Canaria. Most of its nearest relatives are in East Africa. (C.T.G.P.H.)

298 CANARY ARUM LILY   ARACEAE
Dracunculus canariensis Kunth.

A splendid, large but rather rare arum lily, this species is usually found in the forest zones and in shady, damp places in the upper reaches of the lower zone above about 300 m. It occurs on Gran Canaria, Tenerife and all the western islands. It is said to be toxic. (C.T.G.P.H.)

295 | 296
298 | 297

Index to Scientific Names

Index to Common Names